D1174515

Sammy the Sparrow

First and Fastest

Written by Valerie A. Nichols
Illustrated by Margie Segress

Library of Congress: 2003099733
ISBN: Softcover 1-4134-4384-2
Hardcover 1-4134-6528-5

To order additional copies of this book, contact:
Xlibris Corporation
1-888-795-4274
www.Xlibris.com
Orders@Xlibris.com

For Caitlyn, Benjamin, Ariel, and George
who are all first and fastest
in their own way

Sammy the Sparrow loved it whenever his mother told him about the day he was born.

"That crack in the egg you were in kept getting bigger and bigger," his mother would begin. "I thought it would take days and days for you to work your way out, but my! Once you saw that light, you worked and worked until POP! You scratched out of that opening fast!"

Sammy stood tall, fluffed out his feathers and chirped, “I’m Sammy, the first and fastest sparrow around! No bird faster can be found!”

Sammy's good friends Sid and Spence loved flying games. Each day, they would go off to the desert and try new

spirals...

...and zig-zags...

...and swoops.

One game that never changed was the Sammy Race. All the sparrows loved to race each other, but since Sammy always won, Sid and Spence called it the Sammy Race. Birds new to the area always accepted the challenge when Sammy chirped, "I'll race you!" Sammy's friends just watched, waited, and smiled as the race began.

Each race began at the same cactus and finished at the painted rock. The ending of all the races never changed.

Sammy would zoooooomm over the rock, crying, “I’m Sammy, the first and fastest sparrow around. No bird faster can be found!”

Sometimes, Sammy's friends were busy or gone for the day. Then, Sammy would just practice dives and swoops or pretend to have races with birds he saw miles away. He'd choose an object like a saguaro in the distance, look over at the birds, and race to the cactus. The other birds never even knew they were racing, which was just as well, since Sammy still won.

"I'm Sammy, the first and fastest sparrow around! No bird faster can be found!" would ring through the valley.

As if reading his thoughts, Sammy's mom said, "You see, Sammy, these aren't birds. They aren't even animals."

"They're not?" Sammy said slowly. He was still looking up at these enormous gray things. "Well, what are they?"

"I'm not sure, exactly," his mother answered. "But man calls them jets and flies in them. **Man** makes them fly. When they're on the ground, they can't move by themselves."

Man! Sammy knew there were many different kinds of creatures that shared space with birds, but he'd never taken much notice of them before. Now, with his mother next to him, Sammy felt brave and hopped up to one of the creature's feet. It had strange round things instead of claws, and Sammy turned toward his mother.

"How does this *jet* land in a tree?"

"Oh, Sammy!" his mother chuckled. "It's much too big to land in a tree. It would snap it like a twig!"

"Well, then," Sammy continued, still looking at the strange feet, "how does it stand on a mountainside?"

"It can't land in trees or on mountains or on water. It needs a lot of flat land before it climbs up or stops," his mother answered.

His fear completely gone, Sammy began to feel sorry for the strange, huge creatures in front of him.

"Can they swoop around a tree during a race?"

"Not really. They're too big for that. That's why they need a lot of space."

Sammy hopped all over the now quiet creatures. He felt the metal that was so hard compared to his soft feathers.

He tilted his head as he looked at the hard, gray, unbending sticks leading to the strange round feet. Slowly, a smile spread across Sammy's beak.

"So, mother, does this mean I'm still the fastest sparrow in the valley?"

His mother laughed, "Yes, Sammy for now, I guess it does!! But you know you'll always be first with me!"

Chirping with joy, Sammy swooped under, over and around the jets
before he and his mother flew back to their home.

Sammy told Sid and Spence and all his friends about the jets...

...and sometimes, for fun, they all flew like the huge, gray creatures.

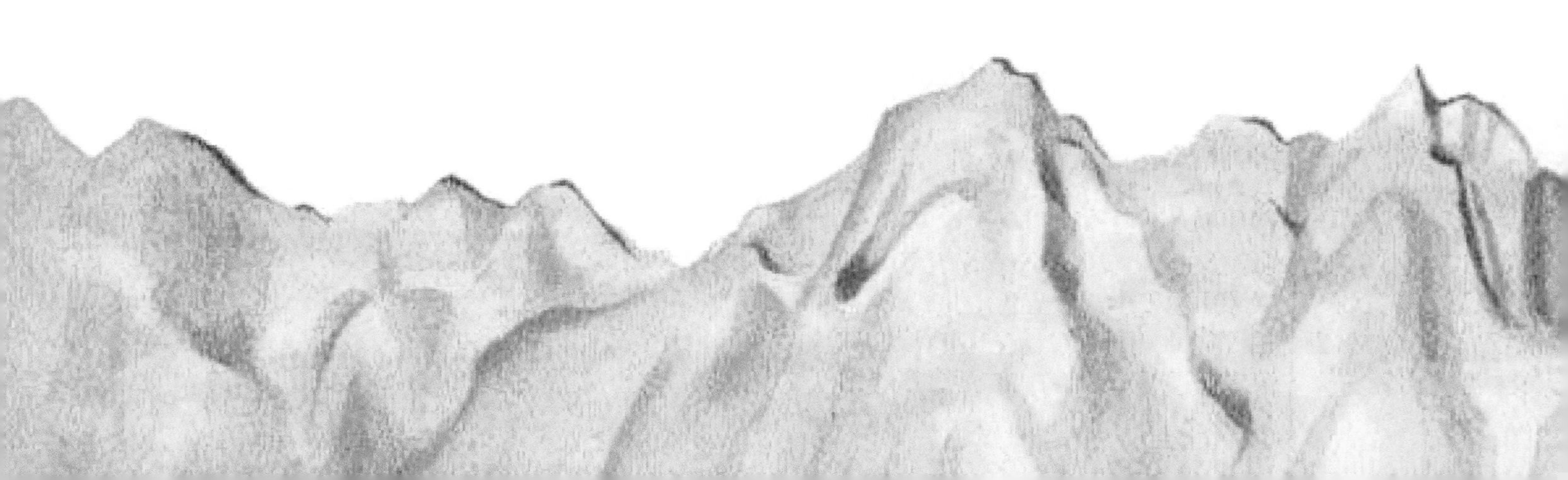

Happier than ever to be a sparrow, Sammy continued his races between the cactus and the painted rock.

And as the sun set behind the mountains, Sammy would fly home, chirping, "I'm Sammy, the first and fastest sparrow around. No bird faster can be found!"

Facts about the F-16 Fighting Falcon

The ‘creature’ that Sammy saw was actually an F-16 Fighting Falcon jet. Luke Air Force Base, in Glendale, Arizona, is the only training facility in the country for pilots flying this type of aircraft.

Even though Sammy thought this metal bird couldn’t do much, it is highly respected by ‘man’! It is highly maneuverable (which means it can move many ways easily!), can fly more than 500 miles before refueling, and is able to fly in all kinds of weather.

It is bigger than a sparrow! It is 49 feet, 5 inches long, 16 feet high, and has a wingspan of 32 feet, 8 inches. It can go as fast as 1,500 miles per hour. No wonder Sammy was shocked!

Edwards Brothers Malloy
Thorofare, NJ USA
March 14, 2014

THE PAIUTE

OREGON
IDAHO
WYOMING
Paviotso
Shoshone
NEVADA
UTAH
COLORADO
PAIUTE
Ute
Hopi
Navajo
CALIFORNIA
Mojave
NEW
MEXICO
Pueblo
ARIZONA
Cahuilla
Pima
Maricopa
Yuma (Quechan)
PACIFIC
OCEAN
BAJA
CALIFORNIA
MEXICO
Gulf of
California

INDIANS OF NORTH AMERICA

THE PAIUTE

Robert J. Franklin
California State University, Dominguez Hills

Pamela A. Bunte
California State University, Long Beach

Frank W. Porter III
General Editor

CHELSEA HOUSE PUBLISHERS
New York Philadelphia

On the cover A Navajo wedding basket made in 1983 by San Juan Paiute Grace Lehi.

Chelsea House Publishers
Editor-in-Chief Nancy Toff
Executive Editor Remmel T. Nunn
Managing Editor Karyn Gullen Browne
Copy Chief Juliann Barbato
Picture Editor Adrian G. Allen
Art Director Maria Epes
Manufacturing Manager Gerald Levine

Indians of North America
Senior Editor Liz Sonneborn

***Staff for* THE PAIUTE**
Assistant Editor Claire Wilson
Copy Editor Brian Sookram
Deputy Copy Chief Mark Rifkin
Editorial Assistant Nicole Claro
Assistant Art Director Loraine Machlin
Designer Donna Sinisgalli
Assistant Designer James Baker
Picture Researcher Margalit Fox
Production Manager Joseph Romano
Production Coordinator Marie Claire Cebrián

3 5 7 9 8 6 4 2

Library of Congress Cataloging-in-Publication Data

Franklin, Robert J.
The Paiute/Robert Franklin and Pamela Bunte.
p. cm.—(Indians of North America)
Includes bibliographical references.
Summary: Examines the culture, history, and changing fortunes of the Paiute Indians.
ISBN 1-55546-723-7
0-7910-0393-0 (pbk.)
1. Paiute Indians. [1. Paiute Indians. 2. Indians of North America.] I. Bunte, Pamela Ann. II. Title III. Series: Indians of North America (Chelsea House Publishers) 89-37072
E99.P2F73 1990 CIP
973'.0497—dc20 AC

CONTENTS

INDIANS OF NORTH AMERICA

The Abenaki
The Apache
The Arapaho
The Archaeology of North America
The Aztecs
The Cahuilla
The Catawbas
The Cherokee
The Cheyenne
The Chickasaw
The Chinook
The Chipewyan
The Choctaw
The Chumash
The Coast Salish Peoples
The Comanche
The Creeks
The Crow
Federal Indian Policy
The Hidatsa
The Huron
The Innu
The Inuit
The Iroquois
The Kiowa
The Kwakiutl
The Lenapes
Literatures of the American Indian
The Lumbee
The Maya
The Menominee
The Modoc
The Nanticoke
The Narragansett
The Navajos
The Nez Perce
The Ojibwa
The Osage
The Paiute
The Pima-Maricopa
The Potawatomi
The Powhatan Tribes
The Pueblo
The Quapaws
The Seminole
The Tarahumara
The Tunica-Biloxi
Urban Indians
The Wampanoag
Women in American Indian Society
The Yakima
The Yankton Sioux
The Yuma

CHELSEA HOUSE PUBLISHERS

INDIANS OF NORTH AMERICA: CONFLICT AND SURVIVAL

Frank W. Porter III

The Indians survived our open intention of wiping them out, and since the tide turned they have even weathered our good intentions toward them, which can be much more deadly.

John Steinbeck
America and Americans

When Europeans first reached the North American continent, they found hundreds of tribes occupying a vast and rich country. The newcomers quickly recognized the wealth of natural resources. They were not, however, so quick or willing to recognize the spiritual, cultural, and intellectual riches of the people they called Indians.

The Indians of North America examines the problems that develop when people with different cultures come together. For American Indians, the consequences of their interaction with non-Indian people have been both productive and tragic. The Europeans believed they had "discovered" a "New World," but their religious bigotry, cultural bias, and materialistic world view kept them from appreciating and understanding the people who lived in it. All too often they attempted to change the way of life of the indigenous people. The Spanish conquistadores wanted the Indians as a source of labor. The Christian missionaries, many of whom were English, viewed them as potential converts. French traders and trappers used the Indians as a means to obtain pelts. As Francis Parkman, the 19th-century historian, stated, "Spanish civilization crushed the Indian; English civilization scorned and neglected him; French civilization embraced and cherished him."

Nearly 500 years later, many people think of American Indians as curious vestiges of a distant past, waging a futile war to survive in a Space Age society. Even today, our understanding of the history and culture of American Indians is too often derived from unsympathetic, culturally biased, and inaccurate reports. The American Indian, described and portrayed in thousands of movies, television programs, books, articles, and government studies, has either been raised to the status of the "noble savage" or disparaged as the "wild Indian" who resisted the westward expansion of the American frontier.

Where in this popular view are the real Indians, the human beings and communities whose ancestors can be traced back to ice-age hunters? Where are the creative and indomitable people whose sophisticated technologies used the natural resources to ensure their survival, whose military skill might even have prevented European settlement of North America if not for devastating epidemics and disruption of the ecology? Where are the men and women who are today diligently struggling to assert their legal rights and express once again the value of their heritage?

The various Indian tribes of North America, like people everywhere, have a history that includes population expansion, adaptation to a range of regional environments, trade across wide networks, internal strife, and warfare. This was the reality. Europeans justified their conquests, however, by creating a mythical image of the New World and its native people. In this myth, the New World was a virgin land, waiting for the Europeans. The arrival of Christopher Columbus ended a timeless primitiveness for the original inhabitants.

Also part of this myth was the debate over the origins of the American Indians. Fantastic and diverse answers were proposed by the early explorers, missionairies, and settlers. Some thought that the Indians were descended from the Ten Lost Tribes of Israel, others that they were descended from inhabitants of the lost continent of Atlantis. One writer suggested that the Indians had reached North America in another Noah's ark.

A later myth, perpetrated by many historians, focused on the relentless persecution during the past five centuries until only a scattering of these "primitive" people remained to be herded onto reservations. This view fails to chronicle the overt and covert ways in which the Indians successfully coped with the intruders.

All of these myths presented one-sided interpretations that ignored the complexity of European and American events and policies. All left serious questions unanswered. What were the origins of the American Indians? Where did they come from? How and when did they get to the New World? What was their life—their culture—really like?

In the late 1800s, anthropologists and archaeologists in the Smithsonian Institution's newly created Bureau of American Ethnology in Washington,

D.C., began to study scientifically the history and culture of the Indians of North America. They were motivated by an honest belief that the Indians were on the verge of extinction and that along with them would vanish their languages, religious beliefs, technology, myths, and legends. These men and women went out to visit, study, and record data from as many Indian communities as possible before this information was forever lost.

By this time there was a new myth in the national consciousness. American Indians existed as figures in the American past. They had performed a historical mission. They had challenged white settlers who trekked across the continent. Once conquered, however, they were supposed to accept graciously the way of life of their conquerors.

The reality again was different. American Indians resisted both actively and passively. They refused to lose their unique identity, to be assimilated into white society. Many whites viewed the Indians not only as members of a conquered nation but also as "inferior" and "unequal." The rights of the Indians could be expanded, contracted, or modified as the conquerors saw fit. In every generation, white society asked itself what to do with the American Indians. Their answers have resulted in the twists and turns of federal Indian policy.

There were two general approaches. One way was to raise the Indians to a "higher level" by "civilizing" them. Zealous missionaries considered it their Christian duty to elevate the Indian through conversion and scanty education. The other approach was to ignore the Indians until they disappeared under pressure from the ever-expanding white society. The myth of the "vanishing Indian" gave stronger support to the latter option, helping to justify the taking of the Indians' land.

Prior to the end of the 18th century, there was no national policy on Indians simply because the American nation had not yet come into existence. American Indians similarly did not possess a political or social unity with which to confront the various Europeans. They were not homogeneous. Rather, they were loosely formed bands and tribes, speaking nearly 300 languages and thousands of dialects. The collective identity felt by Indians today is a result of their common experiences of defeat and/or mistreatment at the hands of whites.

During the colonial period, the British crown did not have a coordinated policy toward the Indians of North America. Specific tribes (most notably the Iroquois and the Cherokee) became military and political pawns used by both the crown and the individual colonies. The success of the American Revolution brought no immediate change. When the United States acquired new territory from France and Mexico in the early 19th century, the federal government wanted to open this land to settlement by homesteaders. But the Indian tribes that lived on this land had signed treaties with European governments assuring their title to the land. Now the United States assumed legal responsibility for honoring these treaties.

At first, President Thomas Jefferson believed that the Louisiana Purchase contained sufficient land for both the Indians and the white population. Within a generation, though, it became clear that the Indians would not be allowed to remain. In the 1830s the federal government began to coerce the eastern tribes to sign treaties agreeing to relinquish their ancestral land and move west of the Mississippi River. Whenever these negotiations failed, President Andrew Jackson used the military to remove the Indians. The southeastern tribes, promised food and transportation during their removal to the West, were instead forced to walk the "Trail of Tears." More than 4,000 men, woman, and children died during this forced march. The "removal policy" was successful in opening the land to homesteaders, but it created enormous hardships for the Indians.

By 1871 most of the tribes in the United States had signed treaties ceding most or all of their ancestral land in exchange for reservations and welfare. The treaty terms were intended to bind both parties for all time. But in the General Allotment Act of 1887, the federal government changed its policy again. Now the goal was to make tribal members into individual landowners and farmers, encouraging their absorption into white society. This policy was advantageous to whites who were eager to acquire Indian land, but it proved disastrous for the Indians. One hundred thirty-eight million acres of reservation land were subdivided into tracts of 160, 80, or as little as 40 acres, and allotted tribe members on an individual basis. Land owned in this way was said to have "trust status" and could not be sold. But the surplus land—all Indian land not allotted to individuals—was opened (for sale) to white settlers. Ultimately, more than 90 million acres of land were taken from the Indians by legal and illegal means.

The resulting loss of land was a catastrophe for the Indians. It was necessary to make it illegal for Indians to sell their land to non-Indians. The Indian Reorganization Act of 1934 officially ended the allotment period. Tribes that voted to accept the provisions of this act were reorganized, and an effort was made to purchase land within preexisting reservations to restore an adequate land base.

Ten years later, in 1944, federal Indian policy again shifted. Now the federal government wanted to get out of the "Indian business." In 1953 an act of Congress named specific tribes whose trust status was to be ended "at the earliest possible time." This new law enabled the United States to end unilaterally, whether the Indians wished it or not, the special status that protected the land in Indian tribal reservations. In the 1950s federal Indian policy was to transfer federal responsibility and jurisdiction to state governments, encourage the physical relocation of Indian peoples from reservations to urban areas, and hasten the termination, or extinction, of tribes.

Between 1954 and 1962 Congress passed specific laws authorizing the termination of more than 100 tribal groups. The stated purpose of the termination policy was to ensure the full and complete integration of Indians into American society. However, there is a less benign way to interpret this legislation. Even as termination was being discussed in Congress, 133 separate bills were introduced to permit the transfer of trust land ownership from Indians to non-Indians.

With the Johnson administration in the 1960s the federal government began to reject termination. In the 1970s yet another Indian policy emerged. Known as "self-determination," it favored keeping the protective role of the federal government while increasing tribal participation in, and control of, important areas of local government. In 1983 President Reagan, in a policy statement on Indian affairs, restated the unique "government is government" relationship of the United States with the Indians. However, federal programs since then have moved toward transferring Indian affairs to individual states, which have long desired to gain control of Indian land and resources.

As long as American Indians retain power, land, and resources that are coveted by the states and the federal government, there will continue to be a "clash of cultures," and the issues will be contested in the courts, Congress, the White House, and even in the international human rights community. To give all Americans a greater comprehension of the issues and conflicts involving American Indians today is a major goal of this series. These issues are not easily understood, nor can these conflicts be readily resolved. The study of North American Indian history and culture is a necessary and important step toward that comprehension. All Americans must learn the history of the relations between the Indians and the federal government, recognize the unique legal status of the Indians, and understand the heritage and cultures of the Indians of North America.

A Chemehuevi Paiute woman and her child, photographed in 1907 by Edward S. Curtis. The Chemehuevi were probably the first Paiute group to come in contact with Europeans.

EXPLORERS, TRADERS, AND SLAVERS

One day Ocean Grandmother came out of the west to the home of Wolf and his younger brother, Coyote. She was carrying a heavy sack, the opening of which was securely tied. Ocean Grandmother then set down her heavy load and told the two brothers that they should carry the sack eastward to Rabbit's country. Wolf said to his brother, "Go ahead, carry this sack to Rabbit. He will tell you what to do with it, so make sure you do not open it until you see him."

With great difficulty, Coyote set off toward the east with the sack, growing ever more curious about its contents. "Maybe it is just sand or dirt, and Ocean Grandmother is playing a joke on us." He felt the sack to see if he could find out what it held, sometimes thinking it was full of snakes or perhaps lizards. Soon Coyote's great curiosity overcame his fear of Wolf's anger. He untied the sack. Immediately, throngs of people began streaming out of the sack, shouting and running away in all directions. Rabbit arrived and said, "Coyote, you fool, why have you done this? This is not where people should live!" There were still a few people left inside the sack. Rabbit took these people to the center of the world, on the north side of the Grand Canyon of the Colorado River. There were plenty of things to eat there, for example, deer, piñon nuts, and agave. The people from the sack liked their new home and decided to stay there. This is how the Paiute came to be living in the center of the world.

The Paiute people, also called the Southern Paiute, today live in 10 communities, 9 of which are located along the north and west side of the Colorado River. The other is on the southwest side of the Colorado River in north-central Arizona and southern Utah. All of these groups share a common language (Southern Paiute), a common history, and a common body of traditions.

The Paiute are related to other Indian groups that live to the north of Paiute territory. These groups are the Shoshone, the Paviotso (also called Northern Paiute), and the Ute. Although the Paviotso are often called the Northern Paiute, they are not closely related to the true Paiute. The Paviotso were first labeled incorrectly in the reports of early pioneers, who mistakenly thought the Indians were Paiute. The Paiute are more closely related to the Shoshone and especially to the Ute.

Before non-Indians began to settle in Paiute homelands in the mid-19th century, the Indians occupied a territory much larger than the scattered lands they now inhabit. Paiute country once formed a great crescent-shaped tract that stretched from southern Nevada and California to north-central Arizona and southern Utah. This territory included the southern portion of the Great Basin in Nevada and Utah, as well as the southwest corner of the Colorado Plateau.

The first Europeans to enter what is now the American Southwest were Spanish explorers seeking treasure. In the early 1500s, Hernán Cortés and his Spanish troops had invaded and conquered the empire of the Mexica, or Aztec, Indians in Mexico, established a colony there, and sent back to Spain several ships laden with Aztec treasures. Soon after, these *conquistadores*, or conquerors, began to look northward for more riches and more territory to colonize. In the 1530s, Spanish colonial officials in Mexico began to receive exaggerated reports of treasure-filled Indian cities to the north—the fabled Seven Cities of Cibola. In order to verify these tales, Spain sent explorer Francisco Vásquez de Coronado in 1540 to explore what is now New Mexico. While there, Coronado sent a party of his men to northern Arizona to visit the Hopi, one of several groups known as the Pueblo Indians and the southern neighbors of the San Juan band of Paiute.

Coronado returned to Mexico in 1541 and gave a less than glowing account of the Pueblo Indians of New Mexico and Arizona. This deflated Spain's dreams of rich conquests. As a result, the Spanish government ceased its exploration of the territory. Not until nearly 60 years later, in 1598, did a Spanish representative, Don Juan de Oñate, reenter the region and officially establish the colonial province of New Mexico. Officially part of Spain, the area then designated as New Mexico included parts of present-day southern Colorado and the Hopi Indian lands in what are now northwestern Arizona and northern New Mexico. The Spanish government soon established several Catholic missions of the Franciscan order in the area in an effort to convert and control the indigenous peoples there. The missionaries for the most part focused their efforts on the Pueblo Indians, including the Hopi, who lived in settled farming villages, or pueblos.

Spanish maps and accounts from the period occasionally describe the country to the northeast of the Hopi Indians as the territory of the "Yutas." The Spanish used the term *Yuta* (from which the state of Utah gets its name) to refer to the Paiute and their neighbors to the east, the Ute. The word derives either from the Ute word *Yutach* or its variant *Yutat*, meaning Ute. When referring to the Paiute, the two groups used another term, pronounced *Payuts* by the Paiute and *Payuch* by the Ute.

A 1657 map of Mexico, the American Southwest, and what was thought to be the island of California. The Paiute lived in the blank area in the north-central part of the map.

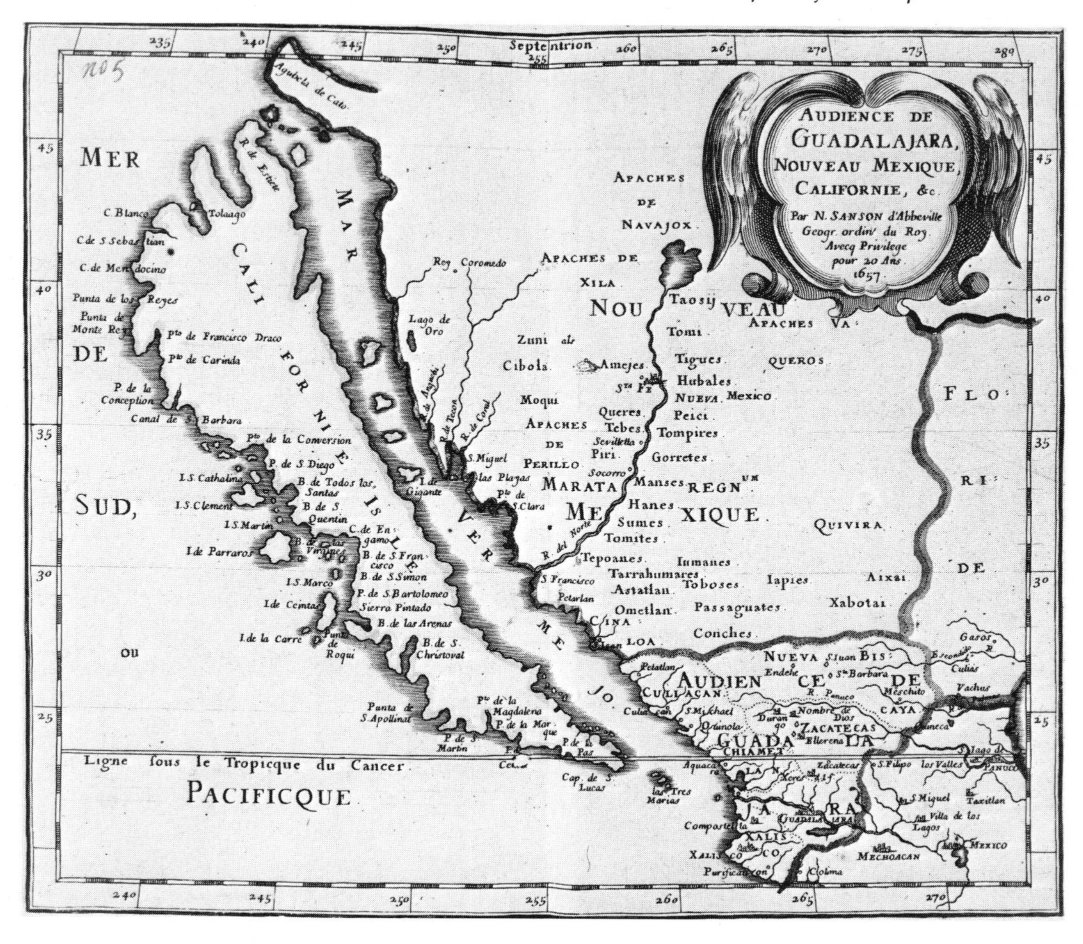

Don José Diego de Vargas was appointed governor of the Spanish colony of New Mexico in 1694. He restored Spanish control to the region after the 1680 Pueblo Indian revolt.

It is not surprising that the Spanish originally thought the Paiute and Ute were one group. Both speak mutually understandable dialects, or variations, of the same language. And before the arrival of the Spanish, the Ute and the Paiute shared a similar way of life, or culture. During the mid-1600s, however, the Ute began to acquire horses from the Spanish and develop what was to become the popular, and greatly idealized, subject of Western film and fiction—the culture of the mounted, buffalo-hunting Great Plains Indians.

In 1680, contact between the Spanish and the southwestern tribes was sharply interrupted. The Pueblo Indians, whom the Spanish had been using as virtual slaves in their missions, dealt a cruel setback to Spain's colonial expansion and the Franciscan missionaries' efforts. Throughout northern New Mexico, the Pueblo Indians, including the Hopi, rose up and drove out the Spanish colonists and missionaries, killing many of them. For a brief period afterward, the Indians retained control of the region.

In 1694, Don Diego de Vargas, the newly appointed governor of New Mexico, restored Spanish domination of the colony but failed to reestablish a mission among the Hopi. Indeed, when the Christianized Hopi village of Awatovi again received Franciscan missionaries in 1701, the Hopi living in the surrounding villages destroyed it and scattered the few surviving inhabitants among the other villages as prisoners. Vargas also found that the Hopi Indians' neighbors—the Yuta, Havasupai, and Navajo—supported Hopi resistance to Spain's attempts at reoccupation. Several decades passed before the Spanish again considered expanding beyond New Mexico.

In the 1760s and 1770s, the Spanish colonial program underwent a brief re-

The San Xavier del Bac Mission was located at the northern frontier of Spain's colony of Sonora. Father Francisco Garcés, one of the priests stationed at the mission, was a member of an expedition that traveled through Paiute territory and met with 40 Chemehuevis in 1776.

newal period. In 1769, the Spanish began to colonize the coast of Alta, or Upper, California. Later, during 1775 and 1776, Fathers Francisco Garcés, Francisco Atanasio Dominguez, and Silvestre Velez de Escalante, three intrepid Franciscan priests, explored the uncolonized Indian country that lay between the older colonial outposts of Santa Fe and Tucson and what are now Monterey and Los Angeles on the California coast. Over the next few decades, Spain established four presidios, or military posts, and a number of Franciscan missions along the coast from San Diego to San Rafael, just north of San Francisco.

The explorer-priests kept journals during their travels, and their accounts provide the first written records of face-to-face contacts between the Paiute and Europeans. Father Garcés was stationed at the mission of San Xavier del Bac. The settlement was located 12 miles south of the presidio at Tucson, the northern frontier of the Spanish colonial province of Sonora. During the winter of 1775–76, Garcés and Lieutenant Colonel Juan Bautista de Anza led an expedition to the San Gabriel mission near Los Angeles. Early in 1776, they crossed the Colorado River into southern California, the territory of the Chemehuevi band of Paiute. There they met with 40 Chemehuevis. According to Garcés, the Indians wore moccasins, antelope-skin shirts, and caps with bird feathers on them. Garcés also reported that the Chemehuevi considered themselves members of the same tribe as the other Paiute bands living to the north.

In another episode of Spanish exploration, Fathers Dominguez and Escalante set out from Santa Fe on July 29, 1776. The purpose of their five-month journey was to discover an overland route to Monterey, California. Dominguez and Escalante traveled in a northeasterly direction through northern New Mexico and western Colorado, and into north-central Utah. The men stopped at the villages of several Ute communities during this leg of their journey. When they reached the Laguna de los Timpanogos, or Utah Lake, they turned toward the southeast and in early October 1776 encountered several Paiute camps and villages there. After visiting with these people, they followed a route down through Utah and across northern Arizona. This portion of their trip ended when they crossed the Colorado River and arrived among the Hopi in northern Arizona in November.

During their journey, the priests kept an invaluable travel diary in which they recorded their impressions of the Indian people they encountered. Dominguez and Escalante distinguished between the various bands of Paiute and the Ute, calling the Paiute bands Yutas Payuchis, or Paiute Ute. They also called them Yutas Cobardes, or Cowardly Ute, because many of these Paiute, unlike the Ute, who were more familiar with Europeans, were reluctant to meet with the Spanish. Many of the

A section of a map, drawn in 1778, that shows the area explored by Franciscan fathers Dominguez and Escalante in 1776. In the central portion of the map are several groups of Paiute villages, identified as Yutas Payuchis by the priests.

Ute spoke some Spanish, so Dominguez and Escalante used them as interpreters during meetings with the Paiute. The priests found that the Paiute "all . . . [spoke] the Yuta language in the same manner as the westernmost Payuchis (San Juan Paiute)," but that the dialect of these Indians was often difficult for the Ute interpreters to understand.

The priests made observations concerning many other facets of Paiute life. During their visit with the Paiute communities of southern Utah, they noted cornfields and provisions of corn and dried squash that the Paiute offered to them. Among the northern Arizona Paiute groups, they recorded the various kinds of wild plant and animal foods that the Indians used. On October 22, 1776, they wrote that the Kaibab Paiute "presented us with two roasted jackrabbits and some piñon nuts." That same evening, when the Paiute discovered that one of the expedition members was sick, "one old Indian from among those present . . . set about to cure with chants and ceremonials." The Catholic priests did not stop the Paiute healer from performing his curing ritual because they did not know at the time that his singing was part of a religious ceremony. The two Spanish fathers preached Catholicism to both the Ute and Paiute, promising to come back to the Indians' territory and establish missions among them. However, this was not to be because the Spanish government decided to focus its energies on Upper California.

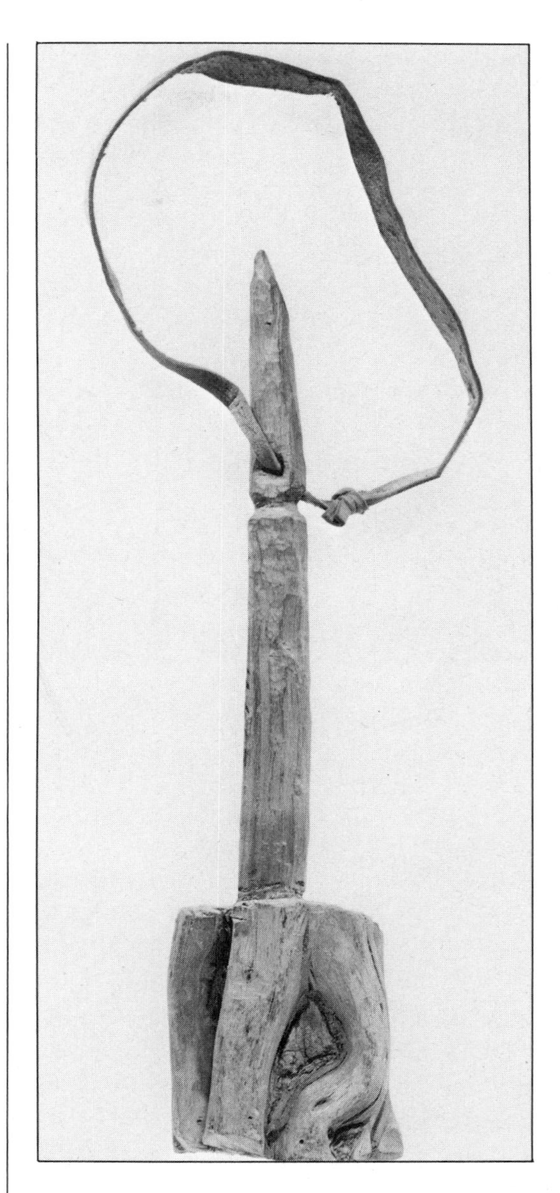

A Paiute war club. During the height of the slave trade in the late 18th and early 19th centuries, the Paiute often engaged in warfare with raiders who sought to capture them for sale in the slave markets located in Santa Fe.

A 19th-century engraving of Captain John C. Frémont. He led the first U.S. military expedition through the Great Basin.

Soon after Dominguez and Escalante's 1776 expedition, Spanish trappers and traders began to use the Colorado and Utah route pioneered by the priests for trading expeditions to the Ute. The traders sought from the Ute beaver pelts and other furs, as well as Paiute captives to sell as slaves in Santa Fe. As a result of increased trade, the Ute, mounted on horses and armed with weapons acquired from the Spanish, began to prey on neighboring Paiute communities in southern Utah. Paiute in the area of present-day Cedar City and Panguitch soon began to conduct their own raids, as well. They invaded the Moapa and Shivwits Paiute settlements farther to the southeast and captured women and children for trade to the Ute, who then traded them to the Spanish. The Paiute slave trade continued after Mexico won its independence in a war with Spain in 1821. Every spring during the height of the slave trade in the early 1850s, Mexican traders brought Paiute captives to Santa Fe, where Indian slaves fetched prices of $100 to $400 each.

Although the Mexicans did not colonize Paiute lands in the Great Basin, they did extend the Dominguez-Escalante route through to Los Angeles during the 1820s. This route, which became known as the Old Spanish Trail, was heavily used by Mexicans. Soon, more and more trails were opened in Paiute territory. In 1827, fur trapper and explorer Jedediah Smith opened a trail from the Great Salt Lake in northern Utah to Los Angeles. And in 1829, Antonio Armijo brought a pack train from Santa Fe to Los Angeles. He traveled across Paiute lands in northern Arizona and southern Utah before reaching a site near the present-day town of St. George on the Virgin River, where he began to follow Smith's route.

After Armijo's trip, annual pack trains traveled the Old Spanish Trail, bringing textiles and other goods to southern California and herds of California horses and mules to Santa Fe. The constant traffic through the heart of Paiute country encouraged more frequent slave raids against the Paiute groups that lived along the trail. The traders grazed and watered their many horses and mules along the trail as well. This probably created a nuisance for Paiute farmers, whose fields of maize and other crops bordered the route between southeastern Utah and Las Vegas, Nevada.

During the 1830s and 1840s, increasing numbers of Americans began to travel through the southern Great Basin. In contrast to the Spanish and Mexican travelers before them, Americans who met with the Paiute often seemed to go out of their way to present a negative picture of the Indians. Among them was Brevet Captain John C. Frémont, who led the first U.S. military expedition along the Old Spanish Trail in 1844. Frémont called the Paiute and other hunting and gathering peoples of the Great Basin "lizard eaters" and "diggers." "Digger" soon became a popular insult for these Indians among American travelers and settlers in the region. According to Frémont, these Great Basin tribes lived "in the lowest state of human existence."

Other visitors to the region often declined to concede that the Paiute were even fully human. One 1839 traveler, Thomas J. Farnham, described the Paiute as if they were animals, living without clothing or houses and even hibernating in the winter:

> Here live the "Paiutes". . . the most degraded and least intellectual Indians known to the trappers. They wear no clothing of any description—build no shelters. They eat roots, lizards, and snails. . . . They provide nothing for future wants. And when the lizards and snails and wild roots are buried in the snows of winter, they are said to retire to the vicinity of timber, dig holes . . . deposit themselves in them, and sleep fast until the weather permits them to go abroad again and hunt for food.

For years to come, the dehumanizing attitude expressed by these early explorers became the basis for many Americans' negative perceptions of the Paiute.

During the 80 years after Fathers Dominguez and Escalante met with the Paiute, many changes occurred in the Indians' way of life. They were mostly for the worse. But in some respects, Paiute life had hardly altered at all. Up until the mid-1850s, historic records show little change in the way the Paiute dressed, the kinds of houses in which they lived, the types of foods they ate, and the ways they obtained their food. Although slave raiding and increased traffic through Paiute territory probably disrupted the Indians' communities to some extent, their way of life appears to have survived the first period of non-Indian contact basically intact. In the ensuing years, however, the Paiute would face changes that they could not have imagined. ▲

Paiute leader Tau-gu and Major John Wesley Powell, photographed in 1873 by John K. Hillers. During the 1870s, Powell and Hillers made the first systematic study of the Paiute Indians' way of life.

PAIUTE DAILY LIFE

The early explorers of Paiute territory recorded many details about the traditional way of life led by the Paiute. For example, their accounts indicate where Paiute people used to live, what types of foods they ate, and how they farmed, hunted, and gathered their foods. But these trailblazers were not always careful or unbiased in their observations. Their descriptions of Paiute life were sometimes superficial or even inaccurate. Therefore, other sources of information must be consulted in order to get a more complete picture of the traditional Paiute society.

Probably the most detailed and accurate accounts of Paiute culture come from the research of anthropologists, scientists who study human society. In the 1870s, Major John Wesley Powell undertook the first truly systematic anthropological study of the Paiute way of life, or culture. Powell is best known for his exploration of the Grand Canyon and especially for his descent down the Colorado River in a wooden boat. But he also performed important fieldwork among the Indians of the region. Powell collected examples of Paiute tools, items of clothing, and other artifacts, many of which are now in Washington, D.C., at the Smithsonian Institution. Powell also brought with him a photographer, John K. Hillers, who took many photographs of the Paiute going about their everyday tasks. Although these pictures were often posed, they still provide a valuable visual record of Paiute communities in the mid-19th century.

In the early 20th century, other distinguished anthropologists, including

Edward Sapir, Julian Steward, and Isabel Kelly, came to study the Paiute. Although these researchers arrived decades after many of the Indians' traditions had already disappeared or changed, they were able to write down the reminiscences of elderly Paiute. They also observed and recorded many aspects of traditional Paiute culture that had not yet disappeared.

Information about aspects of the prehistoric Paiute way of life have been provided by archaeologists, scholars who study the remains of human societies, including tools, buildings, and even ancient garbage. These scientists have been working in the region for nearly as long as anthropologists, uncovering and analyzing the physical evidence of prehistoric Indian life in Paiute country.

The territory that the Paiute traditionally inhabited was vast. The region can be divided into 2 sections, west and east, along a line that roughly follows the 114 degrees west longitude line between Nevada and Utah and northern Arizona. In order to understand the Paiute's way of life and the world in which they lived, it is necessary to first understand this varied geography and the resources it offered.

The groups of Paiute in the west, represented today by the Las Vegas, Pahrump, and Moapa Paiute communities of Nevada and the Chemehuevi Tribe of California, lived in what is now the southeastern corner of Nevada, and in neighboring parts of California, Arizona, and Utah. Much of this area is characterized by terrain called basin and range. Open basins covered with creosote bushes and mesquite trees are divided by mountain ranges that rise in curving wrinkles across the region. Elevated areas between 5,500 and 6,500 feet, such as the slopes of Charleston Peak near Las Vegas or the mountain country by Panaca and Pioche in Nevada, are forested with piñon pine trees. Across the land run ribbonlike oases of fertile floodplain, watered by the Muddy, Virgin, and Colorado rivers. In the days before white settlement, bighorn sheep, and in some places antelope, ranged through the area. Smaller game animals, such as rabbits, jackrabbits, chuckwalla lizards, and desert tortoises, were also plentiful.

The country of the eastern Paiute included present-day southwestern and south-central Utah and northern Arizona. These Paiute are today represented by the five bands of the Paiute Indian Tribe of Utah, the Kaibab Tribe, and San Juan Paiute Tribe. Their traditional homeland is dominated by the high Colorado and Kaibab plateaus and by canyon lands. Canyon lands, such as the Grand Canyon, occur where a plateau has been eroded by water into a broken country of high, flat-topped hills, or mesas, and terraced chasms, or canyons.

Vegetation varies greatly with elevation in this region. High plateau country (elevations of 8,000 to 11,000 feet) is forested with fir, spruce, and aspen. Ponderosa pine is found at lower elevations. There are also wide

Photographer John K. Hillers at one of the Powell expedition campsites in 1875.

expanses of piñon and juniper woodland on the lower plateau slopes and on the rims of canyons 5,000 to 6,500 feet high. Sage and grassland valleys lie at 5,000 feet. In deep-cut canyons that fall to even lower elevations, there are agave, or century plants, and small cacti. In the canyons and river valleys and along the margins of mesas throughout this country are many fertile oases created by springs, rivers, and streams. These areas originally had abundant wildlife similar to that of the basin and range region.

According to the archaeological evidence, the Paiute arrived in the western part of what became their traditional homeland in about A.D. 1000. They most probably expanded into the eastern part soon after. The Paiute, who at that time probably formed a single cultural group with the Ute, were part of a larger expansion of surrounding Indian cultures into the Great Basin that also involved two other major Indian cultural groups—the Paviotso, or Northern Paiute, and the Shoshone. All three groups, Paiute-Ute, Paviotso, and

PAIUTE BAND TERRITORIES IN THE EARLY 1800s

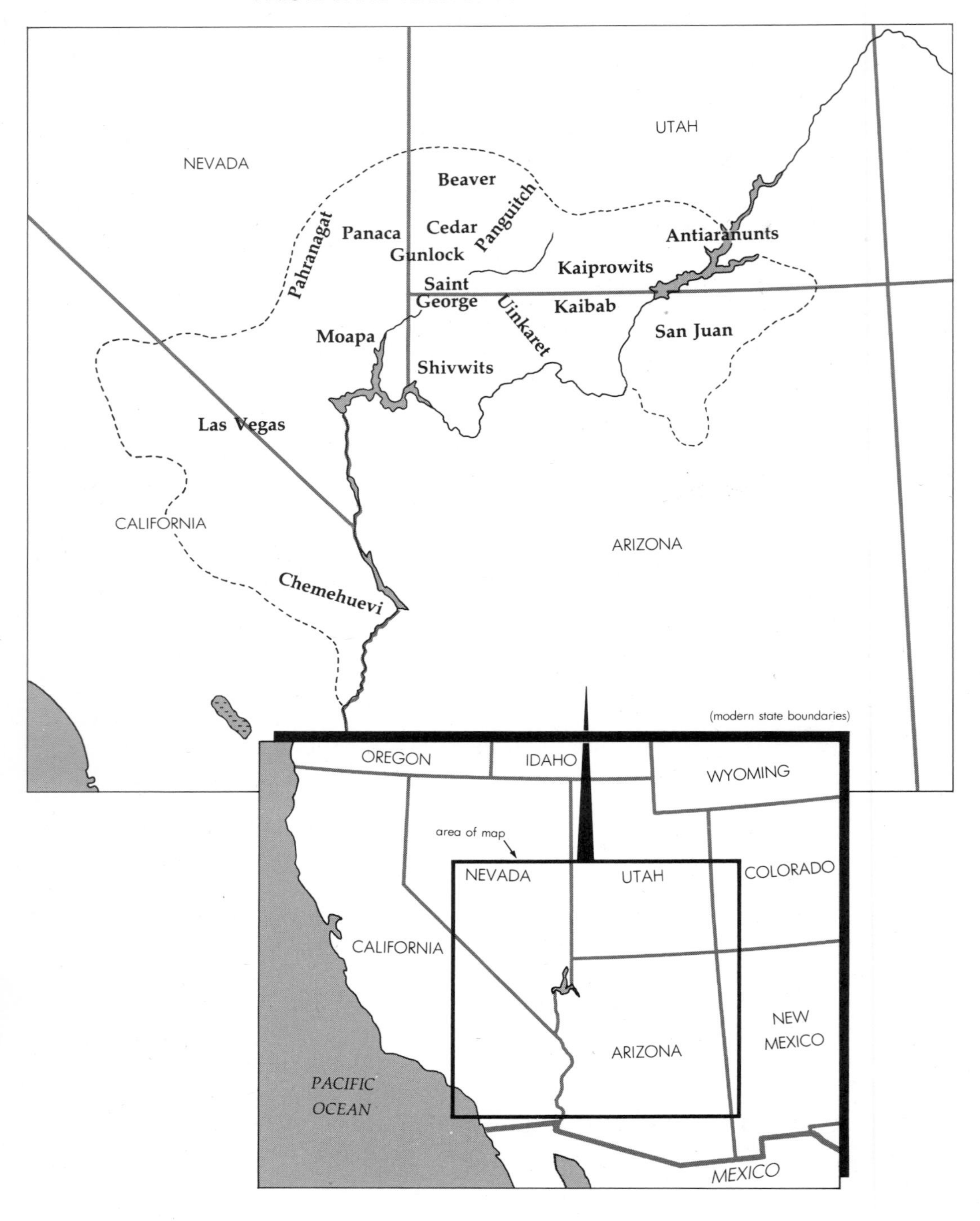

Shoshone, are closely related in language and culture. Scholars call these groups the Numic peoples because they all speak languages classified as members of the Numic language family. The Numic peoples of the Great Basin, including the Paiute, probably originated in southern California, where related Numic peoples, such as the Kawaiisu and the Panamint Shoshone, continue to live today.

The region of the Great Basin and the Colorado Plateau into which the Paiute expanded was already occupied by peoples of two older traditions, the Western Anasazi and Fremont cultures. The Western Anasazi peoples had lived in the region since approximately A.D. 300. The Fremont culture dated from about A.D. 900. Both the Anasazi and Fremont peoples lived in small villages made up of several small houses. Some Anasazi dwellings were pit-houses—circular dwellings with a pole frame and sloping reed-mat walls covered with earth that were constructed partially below ground level. During the latter part of their occupation of the area, the Western Anasazi built rectangular houses with ground-level foundations and walls of adobe masonry and rock.

The Anasazi and Fremont produced fine pottery, some of which was traded to other peoples. Both groups also made their living by growing corn, or maize, and other crops, and by hunting and gathering wild plant and animal foods. Like the Paiute after them, the Anasazi and Fremont probably depended on these wild foods, especially piñon nuts, as much as they did on corn and other cultivated plants.

The Western Anasazi and Fremont traditions began to decline in about A.D. 1150 and were no longer present in the area by A.D. 1250. The Paiute coexisted with these 2 cultures for only about 200 years. It is not known why or how the Fremont and Western Anasazi traditions disappeared from the region, although some scholars have theorized that the Paiute expansion may have hindered trade or disrupted the life of these peoples in some other way.

There is some evidence to support this theory. It is based on the Paiute's relationship with the Hopi Indians, who live to the southeast of the San Juan band of Paiute in northern Arizona. The Hopi carried the Western Anasazi tradition into historic times and were often at war with the Paiute during the 18th and early 19th centuries. The root of the conflict lay in the continued expansion of San Juan Paiute into Hopi territory.

The Paiute took full advantage of the varied resources offered by the natural environment of the southern Great Basin. During their 1776 visit to Paiute territory, Dominguez and Escalante described the cultivation practices of the Indians. They reported that some Paiute groups in Utah and northern Arizona did not farm. But many Paiute communities, perhaps most in both the eastern and the western portions of their range, farmed the fertile lands around springs and along rivers. The priests noted that the Paiute in villages

A Paiute family near their home at Kaibab Plateau in Arizona, photographed in 1873 by John K. Hillers.

along the Virgin River and its tributaries in Utah "devote themselves to the cultivation of Maize." The travelers called the people Parussi Paiute, mistaking the Paiute word for the Virgin River, which was Parus (White Water), for the name of the several communities that lived and farmed the area.

In mid-October, while the expedition was traveling along Ash Creek near present-day Toquerville, its members came across one such farm. Its Paiute owners were absent, possibly because they were away in the mountains gathering piñon nuts. The priests' journal recorded that at the farm they found

> a well-constructed primitive pergola [arbor] with plenty of ears and shocks of maize which had been placed on top. Close to it, on the brief bottoms and bank of the river, were three small maize fields with their well-dug

irrigation ditches. The stubbles of maize which they had harvested this year were still standing.

According to historical records and the accounts of the Paiute themselves, the Indians cultivated a number of crops besides corn. Their food crops included squashes, pumpkins, muskmelons, watermelons, tepary beans, and sunflowers. The Paiute also raised for their seeds two herbs that are less well known to modern Americans—amaranth and chenopodium. Some Paiute grew wheat as well, but they did not do so until the late 18th century or early 19th century. The Paiute apparently acquired it from the Mojave or other Indians who lived farther down the Colorado River. These Indians had themselves been introduced to wheat by the Spanish. The Paiute also grew devil's claw for use in making and decorating basketry. The devil's claw plant has elongated seedpods, the black outer skin of which Paiute women peeled off and used to make designs when weaving baskets.

Paiute methods of agriculture were relatively simple. They planted crops and dug irrigation ditches using only digging sticks with either pointed or spadelike ends. The Paiute would often leave their fields for days or weeks, returning to them only to weed or to harvest. Sometimes, elderly people and young children remained behind to watch the fields while the adults and older children engaged in other daily tasks.

Farming was only one aspect of the Paiute's yearly food-getting activities. They also made many expeditions to hunt and to gather wild animal and plant foods. These journeys took the people to many different locations at different seasons of the year. In the spring, in addition to preparing their fields, Paiute would travel to the open valleys to gather seeds and leafy greens that ripened early. Although Paiute women had the main responsibility for gathering, men often accompanied and helped them. In the summer, they gathered other varieties of seeds and berries

An Anasazi pot found at Canyon de Chelly in northern Arizona. During the 11th century, the people of the Anasazi culture may have been driven out of their homeland by Paiute groups moving in from the west.

in the valleys, as well as bulrush and cattail roots and cattail flowers.

When gathering seeds and some kinds of berries, a Paiute woman used a basketry seed beater that was shaped like a tennis racket. With this tool, she would knock the seeds and berries into a burden basket, the large cone-shaped receptacle in which the Paiute carried things. This gathering method allowed women to harvest seeds and berries efficiently and rapidly. After they were acquired, seeds were ground into meal on a grinding stone, or metate. The meal could then be boiled into mush or shaped into flat cakes and baked on the coals of a fire.

Paiute in the east often camped on high plateaus in summer to gather mariposa lily and other roots as well as the

An 1873 photograph of Paiute women carrying burden baskets during a seed-gathering expedition.

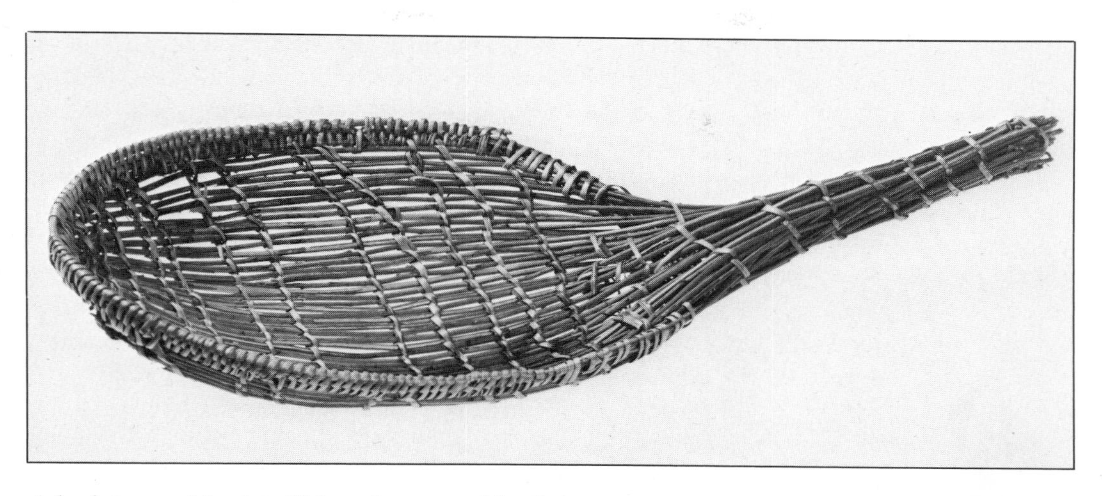

A basketry seed beater. This tool was used by Paiute women to knock seeds into their burden baskets.

elderberries, blueberries, currants, wild strawberries, and other fruits that grew there. In the west, the Paiute traveled to the mesquite tree groves that were scattered along rivers and at spring-fed oases. There they gathered mesquite pods, whose pith, or fleshy inside, is nutritious and has a sweet flavor.

Several times a year, Paiute groups went on expeditions to the places where agave, or century plants, grew. The Paiute removed the top of the plant and then cut off the sharp agave leaves from the edible portion at the base. To cook the agave, the Paiute would lay the stalks in a roasting pit in the ground and bake them for two nights. They also prepared other plants, such as barrel cactus and green corn, in this manner, but baked them for a shorter period. After baking, the agave was made into large, sticky cakes and dried in the sun for several days. The resulting product looked and tasted rather like dried peaches.

In the late summer and fall, the Paiute gathered piñon nuts from the piñon pine forests. In some Paiute communities, men and women would travel to piñon country together and then separate to perform different tasks. The women would gather and grind the nuts and the men would hunt for deer. In other communities, the men and women worked as a team to harvest the piñons. If the pinecones had already opened, the Paiute used poles to knock them down or knock the piñon nuts from them. If the cones had not yet opened, the Paiute would collect them and put them into a fire. This caused the cones to open and release the nuts.

Paiute women roasted the nuts by placing them in a special fan-shaped basket and shaking them together with hot coals. The women cracked the shells by lightly pounding the nuts with a flat mano, or hand stone, on a metate. Then they winnowed, or separated, the shells by tossing the nuts in the air so that the wind or the woman herself could blow the shells away. Women did this with the same tray used for roasting the nuts. Afterward, the seeds were ground into meal and stored for use throughout the rest of the year. The Paiute most often prepared the meal as a porridge, which was one of the staple foods in the Paiute diet. The Indians also stored unshelled nuts for later use.

Paiute women produced their basketry tools, as well as many other practical items, by weaving split and peeled willow and sumac twigs and the leaves of the yucca plant. Among the objects they made were basketry clothing, including sandals and round hats, as well as frames for the cradleboards that they used to hold babies. Paiute women also made basketry water jugs, which they waterproofed with piñon pine pitch, and basketry bowls, which they used when eating meals or boiling foods. In order to boil food, the Paiute would heat stones in a fire and then drop them into a basket filled with liquid, usually water. Paiute women in some communities also made practical brown pottery for cooking.

Paiute men hunted year-round for big and small game animals. They usually tracked large animals, such as deer, in a group rather than alone. These groups of hunters built open-ended corrals from brush in which to trap antelope and sometimes bighorn sheep. Some of the men would drive the animals toward the trap, while others waited to shoot the animals as they milled around in the corral. The Paiute dried most of the meat from big game animals and stored it for later use.

Small game, such as rabbits, beavers, gophers, porcupines, squirrels, quail, and ducks were hunted and trapped throughout the year, either by groups of men or by individuals. Rabbits were probably the most important game animal for the Paiute. A man hunting alone would often track a rabbit to its burrow and poke a stick down the hole until it touched the animal. He would then simply twist the stick into its fur and pull the rabbit out. Groups of men hunted rabbits by surrounding them and killing them with clublike throwing sticks or by driving the rabbits into a row of nets staked to the ground. The Paiute cooked small game whole under the coals of a fire. Even the bones of the animal were crushed and eaten.

Paiute men hunted with bows and arrows made of locust, serviceberry, and other types of wood. Often, men would glue sinew from the leg of a bighorn sheep or deer to the side of the bow opposite the string in order to strengthen its pull. For hunting small game, men used simple arrows made from straightened and sharpened shafts of wood. For large game, they used fletched, or feathered, arrows with flaked-stone or hardwood points. Obsidian, a volcanic glass, was the most highly valued stone for arrowheads and other tools and was considered sacred by the Paiute. Even today, the locations of obsidian quarries are kept secret.

For the Paiute, the winter was a time of little work. Except for occasional rabbit hunts, the people generally lived off the food that they had prepared for storage during the summer and fall. The Paiute came together in their winter villages, played gambling games, and told stories. According to Paiute tradition, many of these stories could be told only in winter. Otherwise, bears and rattlesnakes, who were awake during the rest of the year, would hear and come to bite the storyteller. Winter stories took place in a mythical time before human beings emerged into the world, and almost all of their characters were animals. However, these animals had

A Paiute burden basket collected by John Wesley Powell during his travels among the Indians.

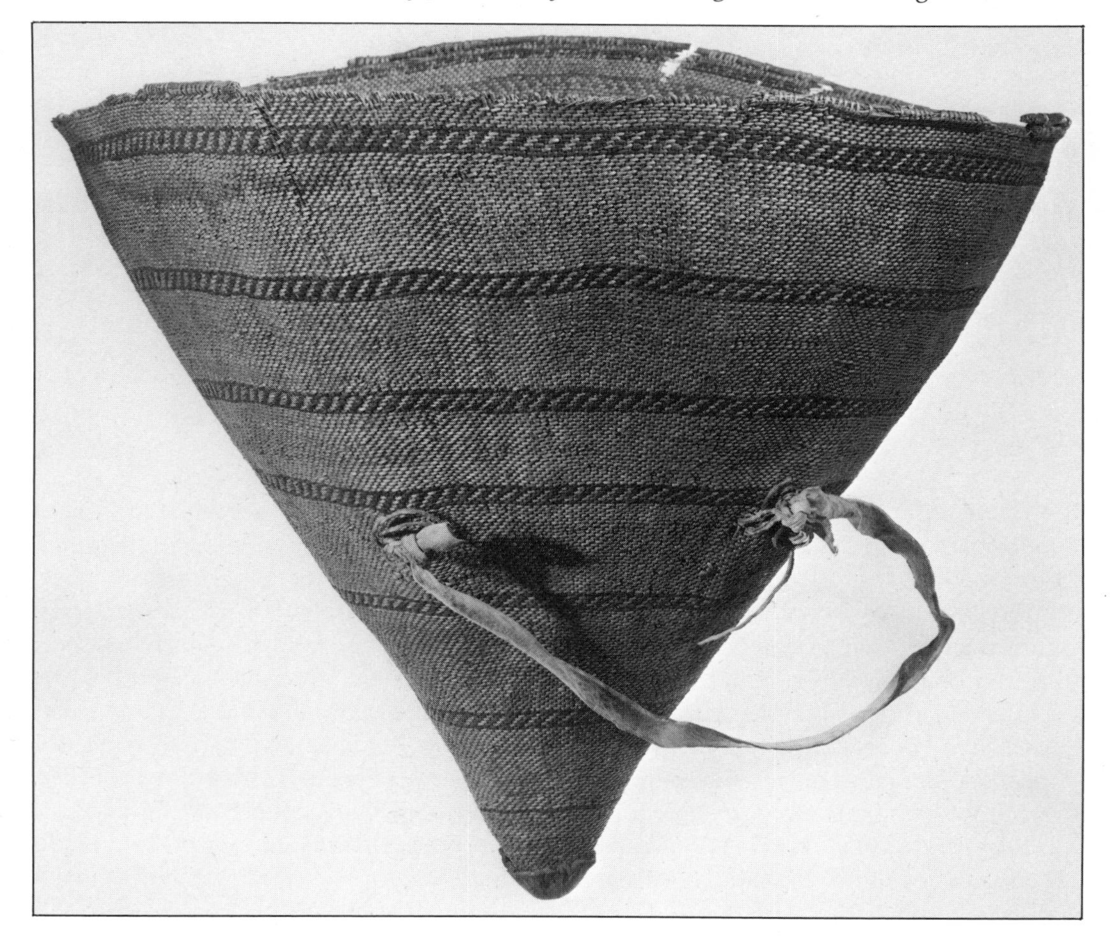

Paiute men playing a traditional gambling game, photographed in 1873.

the bodies of humans, lived in villages and houses, and had other characteristics of people.

Many Paiute stories, such as their creation legend, were about Coyote and his elder brother, Wolf. Wolf did everything in the proper way. Coyote, however, broke every rule and always ended up suffering for it. In one story, Coyote was lazy and only pretended to hunt for his family. He beat his moccasins on a rock and then showed them to his wife to make her believe he had traveled a long way looking for game.

For the Paiute, winter stories were both very funny and very sacred. They often told of how Coyote and Wolf created a particular sacred ceremony or some feature of the natural world. Others were usually devoted to Coyote's humorous sexual misadventures. Despite the sexual content, the Paiute considered such stories suitable for people of all ages. The Paiute believed that their children would laugh at Coyote's clownish behavior and, at the same time, learn the right way to behave from his ridiculously wrong example.

The Paiute played several gambling games at their winter camps and at gatherings held during other times of the year. One of these was the hand game, during which two teams would sit facing each other. Each team took a turn hiding one or more pairs of bone or wood cylinders, called "bones," in their hands. One of the pieces in each pair was marked with a stripe around the middle. While a team was hiding its bones, its members would sing their hand-game songs to give themselves luck and to discourage their opponents. The opposing team would then begin to sing its own songs. Using traditional hand gestures and special words, one of the members of the opposing team would guess which of the other team members' hands held the striped and plain bones. The score was kept by thrusting stick counters made from juniper or other wood into the ground near each team. The two teams would play for valuable goods, including buckskins, horses, and jewelry.

Another popular gambling game was played with stick-dice, flat pieces of wood that were colored on one side and white on the other. A player would strike the dice on a hard stone, usually a metate, making them fly into the air. Like coins in the modern game of heads or tails, each stick would fall to the ground with one side face up. Different combinations of plain and colored sides had different point values. The score was kept in different ways but was usually noted by moving a counter along a row or circle of stones.

The seasonal cycle of Paiute life was also reflected in the types of houses that they built. In the summer, and often in spring and fall as well, people lived under structures with open sides and rectangular roofs of brush that were held up by poles. Sometimes they simply built homes without roofs that had round walls made of brush to keep the wind out or just stayed under trees for shelter. During the winter, they lived in more substantial dwellings. Winter lodges were typically cone shaped, with a main framework of three or four poles interlocked at the top. The Indians then leaned other poles and branches against the framework and covered the walls with juniper bark, rushes, or other materials. During the mid-19th century, these materials were sometimes replaced by animal skin or canvas, a practice that many Paiute adopted from the Indians of the Great Plains. The doorway of the dwelling faced the sunrise, as did the entrance in all other Paiute structures.

By European standards of the time, Paiute clothing was also fairly insubstantial. The typical garment for men and women was a breechcloth or double apron, with front and back flaps. These were usually made of cliffrose bark, although they were sometimes sewn from antelope skin or buckskin.

Shoes were either woven yucca sandals or hide moccasins. In cold weather, Paiute people wore blankets of woven strips of rabbit skin. They also stuffed their moccasins with cliffrose bark or wore badger-skin socks with the fur side turned inward.

At present, there is controversy among anthropologists and historians as to how many Paiute communities, or bands, there were before the arrival of Europeans and what size population and territory each community possessed. Anthropologist Isabel Kelly, who based her conclusions on interviews with elderly Paiute in the early 1930s, believed that the Paiute were divided into some 16 bands or small tribes. Other scholars believe that these bands were not actually unified communities, but were instead composed of many small and completely independent groups, each made up of several families of blood relations. Still others

A tipilike Paiute home. The framework of the structure is similar to that of the Great Plains tipi, but it is covered with brush rather than animal hides.

have theorized that these 16 bands were united into larger political groups by alliances and that the system collapsed as a result of the changes brought on by non-Indian settlement. The evidence is unclear and can in fact be used to argue for any one of these positions.

Scholars are generally in agreement about the type of government and leaders Paiute communities had in this early period. Paiute communities were led by chiefs, called *niavi*. Traditionally, Paiute community chiefs were always men. Women were chosen for other leadership positions in the community and also took part in community meetings. The Paiute usually chose someone from a chief's family to succeed him. For example, the Las Vegas Paiute preferred a father-to-son succession.

In a Paiute community, all the decisions governing that community's affairs were made by its council. In a council meeting, all of the adults in the band would get together to discuss problems within the community or with neighboring groups and to make plans to deal with the problems. The chief would offer advice and suggestions at council meetings, but he always had to carry out the council's decisions. Although a chief had certain specific duties, as a representative of his people, he had no power to make decisions for the community in the way that a dictator, a monarch, or even a president often does. Captain George, a Kaibab Paiute, described to Isabel Kelly in the 1930s what happened when one chief tried to choose his own successor:

This 1873 photo of Moapa Paiute leader Aiattaua is obviously posed. Paiute men and women actually wore fewer articles of clothing.

> A long time ago, before I was born, the father of Kwinivats was chief. He got to be an old, old man, and forgot how to tell the people to hunt. So he told his son he had better be chief. But the people didn't like that and made [another man named] Keno chief [instead].

Throughout Paiute country, chiefs were expected to perform certain duties. One of the most important of these

A Kaibab Paiute council meeting, photographed in 1873 by John K. Hillers.

was the morning speech, during which the chief would announce plans for the day and exhort people to live in harmony with each other. Captain George told Isabel Kelly how Keno used to give his morning speeches:

> Keno spoke early in the morning, standing by the door of his house. He spoke loudly so all could hear from their camps. He told the people how to hunt and where to hunt; and after a time, everybody answered, "Yes." Then they went for deer.

A chief was also expected to act as spokesperson for his community in its dealings with other Paiute communities and with other tribes. Often he would arrange for groups to make exchange visits between neighboring communities. In this way, members of two or more groups could gather food or hunt game in each other's territory and hold traditional round dances together. In a round dance, men and women hold hands and dance a kind of two-step, moving around in a circle while one or more singers sing one song after another, never repeating a song. Often these dances lasted until dawn. Not surprisingly, they were very popular with the young people.

The Paiute community in Las Vegas periodically held a four-day festival in honor of the dead, to which the Paiute and Indians from other communities as distant as present-day San Bernardino, California, were invited for gambling and other pastimes. According to Julian Steward, an anthropologist who interviewed Nevada Paiute in the 1930s, one of a chief's most important duties was to plan and direct this festival. He would announce it six to eight months in advance so that members of other communities could prepare properly. He would also give speeches to the visitors and community members throughout the duration of the festival.

Family relationships and marriage in Paiute society created ties that united each community and cemented alliances between communities. Paiute kinship and marriage practices traditionally were based on different principles than those of modern American society. For example, the Paiute had strong ties of kinship even with relatives that most Americans would consider distant relations. The Paiute often thought of these relatives in the same way that members of mainstream American culture think of their brothers, sisters, aunts, and uncles. The Paiute words for kinship relationships reflected their beliefs. For instance, the Paiute used terms equivalent to "big brother/little brother" and "big sister/little sister" to describe siblings, first cousins, and distantly related cousins. The Paiute also called even the distant cousins of their parents and grandparents by the same terms that they used to address their aunts, uncles, grandmothers, or grandfathers.

The Paiute also believed it was wrong for a person to marry anyone who was related to them by blood, even a very distantly related cousin. Because of this, young people often had to look outside their own community to find a husband or wife. This is one of the reasons that the Paiute often traveled to visit and dance with their neighbors. Such socializing offered an opportunity for young people to get acquainted with potential marriage partners from other communities.

The Paiute had no special marriage ceremony. A man and a woman would just set up housekeeping together. If they found they did not get along, they would simply go their separate ways. The older relatives of young people would often arrange a marriage. This was done to make certain that their younger relative would marry a reliable person who was capable of supporting a family.

Most marriages were monogamous, although on occasion two sisters might share one husband, or two brothers might have a wife in common. When a Paiute spouse died, very often the relatives would try to persuade the widow or widower to marry a relative of the deceased. In this way, children would continue to have two parents to look after them, and the relationship between the two families could be preserved.

The religious life of the early Paiute revolved around two important types of ceremonies. One type was the life-cycle rituals, or rites of passage. For the

Two Paiute couples photographed in the late 1800s.

Paiute, the three most important events in the life cycle of an individual were puberty, the birth of a first child, and death. All three were marked by ritual taboos, or restrictions, and special rites.

At the onset of menstruation, a young Paiute woman underwent a special rite of passage that, in the community, signaled puberty. Her older relatives would build a special house for her away from the main camp. Then they would paint her face and her hair and scalp with white clay or with red-ocher pigment. The girl would receive instruction from them explaining what actions she was to perform and the taboos she was to observe for the next four days of the ceremony. She was told to run to the east every morning before the sun rose. In some communities, she would also have to run west at dusk. She was instructed not to be lazy and to work hard at gathering wood and at other tasks. She was not to touch her face or hair with her hands. Her relatives made a special scratching stick so that she would not have to break the taboo if her face or head itched. She also could not eat meat or salt or drink cold water during the four days. Every night she slept on a hotbed—a shallow depression that her relatives had dug, filled with warm coals, and then covered with earth. At the end of the four-day ceremony, she was fed the liver of a rabbit or another animal wrapped in juniper leaves and other medicinal plants. Her relatives washed her hair, singed the ends of it, and burned her old clothes.

The purpose of this rite of passage was twofold. First, the Paiute believed that running to the east and following the prescribed taboos would magically help the girl to grow up healthy and lead a long and productive life. Secondly, the instructions her elders gave her, coupled with the discipline of the taboos, the hard work, and the isolation from other children, served to impress on the girl that she was no longer a child. She was now on her way to becoming a responsible adult.

For an adolescent Paiute boy, puberty was marked by hunting taboos and rituals. Until he was old enough for marriage, he, his mother, his father, and any girl or young woman who had reached puberty were forbidden to eat any game that he had killed. The boy was encouraged to give his catch to old people in the community. If he did not observe this taboo, he would grow up weak and lazy, and the game animals would not permit themselves to be caught by him when he hunted. When he was considered old enough to marry, in his mid to late teens, his elders would wash and singe his hair, paint his head with red pigment, and lift the hunting taboo.

When a married couple had their first child, the couple underwent a rite of passage similar to the girl's puberty rite. Both the husband and the wife observed taboos that forbade them to scratch their head and face, eat meat or salt or drink cold water. The husband also had to run to the east each morning and was encouraged to gather wood and perform other tasks.

At the death of a community member, the relatives would prepare the body, sometimes wrapping it in buckskin or painting the corpse's face with red pigment, and then either bury or cremate it. Most often, the deceased was buried in the house where he or she had died. Occasionally, the body was cremated by burning the house. Less often, the corpse was taken away from the camp and covered with rocks on a ledge or in a cave.

The Paiute abandoned any dwelling in which a death had occurred, whether or not the person was buried within it. The dead person's possessions were buried or burned and his horses and dogs were killed. In some cases, community members would also kill a child or another relative of the deceased to keep a dead person company in the next world. The mourners singed or cut their hair and abstained from meat and salt for four days following the funeral.

The other important group of Paiute rites were those that honored the spirits of the natural world. The Paiute prayed and conducted rituals to influence the spirits of nature and show their respect and gratitude to them. In the Paiute view of the natural world, there were many supernatural beings, but one was more powerful than all the others. The Paiute often called it simply Thuwipu Unipugant, or the One Who Made the Earth. The sun was one visible manifestation of this spirit. Most Paiute prayed to the sun at sunrise and sometimes at noon or sunset. At daybreak, they would cast some cornmeal or some ashes from their fire toward the sun, asking it to take away any evil dreams they had had during the night and to make their day a good one. The Paiute also associated the mythical heroes, Coyote and Wolf, with this powerful spirit, seeing the good and virtuous

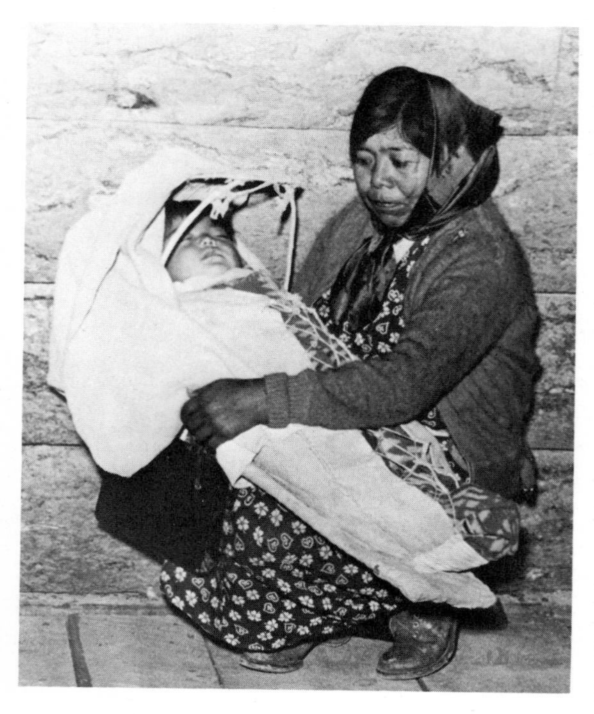

A Paiute woman carrying her baby in a cradleboard. This device allowed women to keep their infants close to them while they performed their daily chores.

Wolf and the wicked and silly Coyote as two necessary sides of the same all-powerful creator.

The other supernatural beings who inhabited the Paiute world all had lesser degrees of power. The Thunder People, who lived in the clouds, brought thunder and rain every year in early summer. The mermaidlike Water Babies lived in certain lakes or rivers and would drown unsuspecting people who came too close to the water. According to the Paiute, spirits inhabited every type of food, medicinal plant, and game animal.

The Paiute prayed to many of these spirits. In the spring or early summer, when thunder was heard for the first time after the winter, the Paiute would build bonfires and ask the Thunder People to bring rain and not harm anyone. During gathering or hunting expeditions, they would pray to plants and animals before harvesting these resources. The Paiute thanked their quarry, asking it to be good food or good medicine for them. Otherwise, the plant or animal would not give its special power to the people or might prove difficult to find the next time it was needed. Indeed, there were special taboos involving the use of many plants and animals. For example, deer hides could not be tanned in the presence of children, and only a person born in the summer could watch over agave as it baked during the night.

If a Paiute became ill, he or she would look to a medicine man, or healer, for a cure. Such a person was called a *puagant*, which meant "one who has sacred power." A puagant usually had one or more animal spirit helpers. A spirit helper might be an eagle, a porcupine, a squirrel, or some other animal that the puagant had dreamed of or had encountered in some other magical way. He would pray to this animal, perform magic rituals with its feathers or fur, and might even capture one to keep as a pet. These animal spirits were believed to assist medicine men in healing the sick or in causing illness and death through spells and witchcraft.

According to one Paiute story, a medicine man was once called to cure a dying woman whose village was many miles away. The puagant knew that the woman was going to die before he could get there, so he sent his eagle spirit helper over the mountains ahead of him. He instructed it to catch her spirit as it was leaving her body and hold it until he arrived. In this way, the eagle spirit kept the woman alive until the man came and healed her.

The traditional Paiute way of life lasted for many hundreds of years. But it was to change drastically starting in the 1850s and 1860s, as ever-increasing numbers of American pioneers began to stream into Utah, Nevada, and northern Arizona. As the Paiute struggled to adapt to these new circumstances, they managed to preserve some elements of their culture. Much more, however, was lost or altered forever. ▲

An 1849 cartoon that reflects the mood of many Americans toward California in the mid-19th century. When gold was discovered there, hundreds of easterners flocked to the West in search of a quick profit. During their journey, many fortune hunters passed through Paiute territory, disrupting the Indians' farms and lives.

PAIUTE, MORMONS, AND MINERS

In 1848, gold was discovered in California, beginning what is known as the gold rush. In the years that followed, dozens of prospectors, or forty-niners, traveled through Paiute territory on their way to the goldfields. Some journeyed from Salt Lake City to Los Angeles on the route pioneered in 1827 by Jedediah Smith, an early white explorer of the American West; others traveled the Old Spanish Trail from Santa Fe. The majority of the forty-niners were unconcerned about the lives of Indians, and they often shot at the Paiute and pilfered from their fields. Outgunned and on foot, the Paiute generally tried to stay out of the way. Even when it was evident that the Paiute were avoiding them, the prospectors often believed that the Indians posed a threat to their wagon trains. William Farrer, a young forty-niner, wrote in his diary on November 3, 1949:

> . . . found Indian wigwams close by camp recently vacated by the[m]. Pot made of earthen ware being on the fire a bow laying close by the inhabitants had left upon hearing us. We are now in the Pah Utah [Paiute] territory & as they are notorious for their depredations, we had to be very vigilant.

Although the Paiute had many opportunities to attack and kill straying members of the white men's wagon trains, the major complaint the forty-niners reported was the theft of some of their livestock. From the Paiute standpoint, the travelers' cattle was trespassing on their land. The Paiute probably believed they had a right to take livestock that wandered near their farms and camps. But the forty-niners gave little thought to the Indians' point of view. They shot at and sometimes killed Paiute whenever they believed that the Indians threatened their livestock.

Some forty-niners gave more positive reports of the Paiute. For example, George Q. Cannon described a valley with 20 acres of Paiute fields:

> We judged the Indians had raised good corn there. About three miles further down we came to another small valley. There was a corn field there also, in which the corn stalks were standing; the ears had been stripped off. Morning glories, and beans, squash vines, and other vegetables had grown in the field, and had been well cultivated. Large ditches had been made for irrigating purposes, which gave evidence of industry and perseverance.

However, non-Indian travel through a few Paiute farming areas became so heavy that some Paiute probably had to abandon fields that were too close to the trail.

During the gold rush era, another group of non-Indians began to arrive in the region to the north of Paiute country. In 1847, Brigham Young, a former painter from Vermont, led a group of settlers into the Great Salt Lake area. These new pioneers aimed to settle there in a self-sufficient farming colony rather than just pass through.

The settlers were followers of a persecuted religious sect, the Church of Jesus Christ of Latter Day Saints, of which Young was the president. By 1849, enough new converts had arrived in Salt Lake City from Europe and the eastern United States to begin a further expansion of the colony. These new arrivals, called Mormons, were soon exploring Paiute territory in what are now southern Utah and southern Nevada for good settlement sites. Brigham Young hoped to establish a string of Mormon settlements from Salt Lake City to Los Angeles. In doing so, he expected to take advantage of the business opportunities provided by travelers on their way to Los Angeles.

The Paiute reaction to the early Mormon colonies in their territory was ambivalent. Although the Mormons provided the Paiute with some protection from the forty-niners and the slave raiding of the Ute, the Paiute must have worried about sharing their resources. They responded to the Mormons' early exploration by taking the settlers' livestock. In 1851, George A. Smith, who had led a Mormon colonial expedition into Paiute territory in 1850, wrote a letter to the editor of the *Desert News* stating that the Indians "imagine they have a right to our cattle, for they have foreclosed on a number of them." Other Paiute, although wary, accepted the Mormons' presence because of the protection and trading advantages it afforded. Backed by the Mormons, the Las Vegas Paiute returned to their Las

NON-INDIAN EXPLORATION ROUTES THROUGH THE SOUTHWEST, 1776–1844

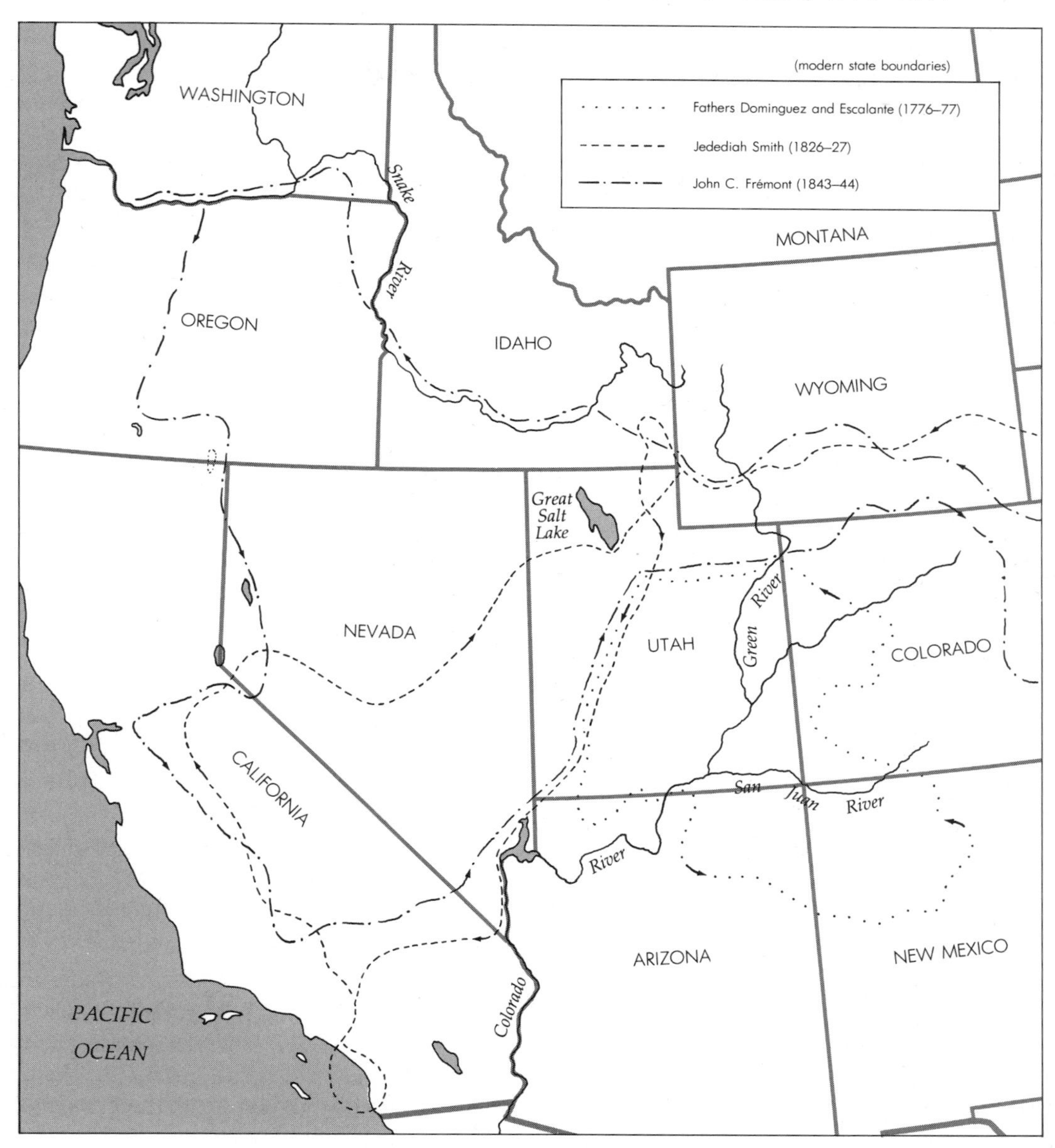

Vegas spring homeland in 1855 after having abandoned the area in the late 1840s because of their fear of the forty-niners.

The Mormons rapidly colonized Paiute territory. By the end of 1858, barely 11 years after the first Mormons arrived, there were more than a dozen

Mormon settlements in the region. The Mormons, in many cases, had simply displaced the Paiute farmers and set up their own colonies on the Indians' irrigated fields. By 1859, Mormons controlled much of the Virgin River floodplain in southern Utah. They had settlements along the Virgin River, as well as along its two major tributaries, Ash Creek and Santa Clara Creek.

Ironically, as the Mormon colonists sought to take over the Paiute's best farmland, the industrious Paiute began to help them set up colonies. Their aid proved indispensable. The Paiute helped construct buildings, prepare fields, and even wash the Mormons' clothes. The Mormons in turn acted as a buffer between the Paiute and the steadily increasing numbers of wagon trains that passed through their territory. Unlike the forty-niners, the Mormons were under strict instructions to establish peaceful relations with the Paiute. Brigham Young told the members of his church that it was better to feed the Indians than to fight them. Some Mormons learned to speak the Paiute language, and others distributed surplus food to the Indians. The settlers must have seemed good neighbors at the time, but the Paiute would have undoubtedly been less accommodating if they had understood the future consequences of the Mormon invasion. Perhaps the most devastating of these was to result from something that the Mormons unwittingly brought with them—disease.

Brigham Young, president of the Church of Jesus Christ of Latter Day Saints, better known as the Mormon church. He and his followers established the first permanent non-Indian settlements among the Paiute.

Before the Mormons arrived, the Paiute had undoubtedly been infected by some European diseases. From the 16th through the 19th centuries, most Indian groups in the Southwest had been victims of such illnesses. Some of these tribes, particularly the Pueblo peoples in New Mexico and Arizona and the Mojave and Pai peoples of southern California and northern Arizona, were trading partners of the Paiute. All of them had suffered serious epidemics of smallpox, typhoid, and measles. Although there is no direct evidence that these diseases were passed on to their trading partners, it is likely that at least some of these epidemics also reached the Paiute. The Indians probably also contracted cholera and other diseases directly from non-Indian travelers on the Old Spanish Trail.

During the decade or so following Mormon settlement, it is certain that the Paiute in southern Utah and Nevada were stricken with disease. The Mormon settlers themselves suffered from epidemics of cholera, scarlet fever, whooping cough, measles, mumps, tuberculosis, and malaria. Because the Paiute were living nearby, all of these diseases were immediately passed on to them. Such diseases had been unknown in North America before the arrival of Europeans. Therefore, the native peoples had not developed immunities to them and were hit especially hard.

Deadly diseases also contaminated the water supply in the afflicted region.

Two Chemehuevi Paiute pose outside their house, which is made of arrow reed.

Members of a Mormon family posing outside a building at a Mormon dairy in Arizona Territory in 1887.

In settlements where Mormon community members drank from their irrigation ditches, many people were infected from the water. The Mormons often built their settlements upstream from Paiute villages, and disease was often borne by the water into the Indians' settlements. As a result, the Paiute also suffered from devastating outbreaks.

In 1856, an epidemic, possibly of mumps, swept across a number of Paiute villages. This episode was still remembered in the 1930s by some Moapa Paiute from one of the stricken settlements. They told anthropologist Isabel Kelly that "there were so many deaths that instead of receiving regular burial, the corpses were dumped into a near-by gully." A Kaibab Paiute who was a child during the Mormon settlement period added, "After the Mormons came, all the Indians died." The various diseases quickly depopulated most Paiute communities. Although the actual number of people that died cannot be known precisely, some Paiute settlements probably lost three-quarters of their inhabitants by the mid-1870s.

During the late 1850s and early 1860s, new waves of settlers with much less tolerant attitudes toward Indians than the Mormons began to arrive in Paiute territory. Miners came to exploit gold, silver, copper, and lead sources. A new generation of farmers and ranchers, both Mormon and non-Mormon, also arrived to take the remaining Paiute land.

Miners were generally out to make a quick profit. Typical 19th-century mining towns in California, the Great Basin, and elsewhere were lawless places, and the inhabitants were notoriously ruthless in their treatment of Indian people. The miners who came to Paiute territory proved to be no exception.

In southern Nevada, most mines were "discovered" with the aid of Paiute guides who had known about and used them for many years before the white miners arrived. A number of these sites were large enough to be commercially successful, and mining towns soon developed around them.

The inhabitants of the towns took most of the Indians' property, forcing the majority of the Paiute into ghettolike camps on the edges of Pioche, Panaca, and other newly founded towns. The Paiute formed a pool of unskilled laborers and were often paid only in food and cast-off clothing for their very difficult labor. Rather than respecting the Indians for their willingness to work hard, the miners generally had a very low opinion of the Indian people they exploited.

Newspaper accounts and other sources provide a great deal of information about the relations between the Paiute and the early settlers in southern Nevada. One reported incident in the Pahranagat Valley in the late 1860s resulted in bloodshed. It was said to have started when a group of Indians killed two young white men on a wagon road about six miles west of Hiko, Utah. The Indians were apparently never given an opportunity to tell their side of the story. Instead, two Indians, who may or may not have been the guilty ones, were "apprehended" and hung. The colonists then raided 2 Paiute camps at daybreak, killing 17 people at each one.

On April 16, 1878, the *Pioche Record* reported another incident. The story noted that "on Saturday an Indian was shot and killed in Pahranagat Valley by Mark Moore and another tied up and whipped. The Indians had been breaking into houses and killing cattle." The report went on to make derogatory mention of two Paiute men who did odd jobs in the town. "The two great warriors of Pioche have put on their warpaint and are eager for the fray. At them T-I-G-E-R-S."

The growing mining camps needed a continuous supply of provisions. As a result, non-Indian farmers moved into and took over any land that could be irrigated. The Paiute already had some of these stream- or spring-fed oases under cultivation and had maintained others for the plant and animal resources they supported. The mining camp settlers paid no heed to the Paiute's prior claims to these lands and took over as much as they could.

As the Paiute lost their fields in Nevada, Utah, and Arizona, they tried various survival strategies. They relied more heavily on hunting and gathering, farmed on land that the white settlers considered worthless, and tried to find employment in Mormon and non-Mormon settlements. Unfortunately, the settlers took over or destroyed more than the Paiute's farming areas. Mormon, and later non-Mormon, ranchers brought in thousands of head of cattle to graze on grasses that the Paiute traditionally relied on for seeds. And to obtain wood for their fences, houses, and firewood, the new settlers felled large stands of piñon pine trees, whose nuts had been another staple in the Paiute diet.

New waves of Mormon settlers began to arrive in the 1860s after the original settlers had already displaced many of the Paiute. Eventually, enough Mormons had moved into the area so that they no longer needed or desired the

Indians' help to survive. For a short time in the late 1860s, the Mormons in Kaibab country continued to encourage the Indians to live near their settlements. The Mormons needed these "friendly" Indians to protect them from raids by the Navajo to the south. But the Mormons later made peace with the Navajo and thereafter did not require even this small amount of assistance from the Paiute.

By the 1870s, the Paiute who lived near Mormon settlements had become destitute and unwanted. Their traditional resources had been depleted by the earlier waves of settlers. Many Paiute were starving and thus became especially susceptible to diseases. The newly arrived Mormon settlers knew nothing of the Paiute's helpfulness to the earlier pioneers and therefore did not feel responsible for the plight of the Indians.

In 1872, explorer and ethnologist Major J. W. Powell wrote that "the Pah-Utes prowl about, begging, doing odd jobs, and selling Indian trinkets. Short in stature, half starved, scantily-clothed, they present a pitiful, abject appearance." A year later, Powell and George W. Ingalls, Indian agent for the Moapa Paiute Reservation in Nevada, traveled through Paiute territory as special Indian Service commissioners. Upon their return, they presented a report on their investigation of the status of the Indian groups of the Great Basin. In their report, they recommended that the U.S. government create a reservation (a tract of land specifically set aside by the federal government for the use of Indians) in order to provide the Paiute with land for farming and food supplies.

In 1873, President Ulysses S. Grant signed an executive order that was to reserve a large part of southeastern Nevada for all the Paiute. In 1874, the boundaries were changed slightly, expanding the tract to about 2 million acres, including more than 6,000 acres of irrigable land. Impoverished Paiute bands in other areas soon learned of the U.S. government's intentions. These groups were so desperate for resources that they agreed to relocate from their homelands to southern Nevada if they were provided with farmland. A proud people, the Paiute were eager to be able to support themselves again.

However, the government never put its plan into practice. Before the reservation was officially created, a non-Indian Moapa River valley settler persuaded Congress to change the boundaries of the land grant. Within 1 year, the tract was reduced to a mere 1,000 acres, of which only a small portion was irrigable.

When the Paiute learned of the drastic reduction in size of the Moapa reservation, most bands no longer saw any advantage in moving there. Even the tiny part of the reservation that could be irrigated was of little use because local non-Indian stock owners allowed their cattle and horses to wander throughout the reserved land. The few Moapa Paiute who did move to the reservation were unable to farm, and their

Members of Paiute and Mormon communities meet with the U.S. commission sent to Paiute country in 1873 to investigate disputes between the two groups. The federal team was led by John Wesley Powell, who stands at the far left.

attempts at raising livestock were thwarted by the neighboring stock owners. These non-Indian ranchers continually stole the cattle the government provided for the reservation Indians. In 1880, James Spencer, the U.S. government's agent, or representative, on the Moapa reservation wrote:

> The Indians are scattered over the surrounding country for 200 miles around, eking out a precarious existence by working, begging, root-digging, and insect-eating—a life not of their choice.

In the same year, Jacob Hamblin, a Mormon missionary who ministered to the Hopi and later to the Navajo, wrote to Powell regarding the Kaibab band's need for assistance from the federal government. The missionary reported:

A Paiute man and his daughter outside their home in 1872. The man was described as an arrow maker by photographer Clement Powell.

> The Kanab or Kaibab Indians are in very destitute circumstances; fertile places are now being occupied by the white population, thus cutting off all their means of subsistence except game, which you are aware is limited. They claim that you gave them some encouragement in regard to assisting them [eke] out an existence.

Powell merely responded that the Paiute ought to go to the Moapa reservation or to live among the Uintah band of the Ute on their reservation. He said that only those Indians who reported to U.S. government Indian agencies would be assisted.

Neither destination offered a solution for the Kaibab Paiute. Not only was the Uintah Ute reservation outside of the Paiute's traditional territory, it was also the residence of the very enemies who had in the past conducted slave raids on the Paiute. The now tiny Moapa reservation could not even support the Moapa Paiute, much less additional Kaibab refugees. The Paiute would have to wait until the 20th century before they would receive more assistance from the government.

The San Juan Paiute, who lived to the east of the Colorado River, were destined to have a history very different from that of the Paiute bands to the west. In the early 1870s, Mormons began to settle what is now Tuba City, Arizona, in the San Juan Paiute homeland. Unlike the settlers of other regions of the Paiute homeland, the Mormon farmers in San Juan Paiute territory remained in one area. The Mormons did not extensively expand their settlements, and the Paiute were able to keep much of their most fertile farmland. For a time, the Indians and the Mormons farmed in some of the same areas and even shared irrigation water. By the mid-1880s, however, the increasing Mormon population began to put pressure on the local Paiute and Hopi settlements.

In response to indications of problems between the Mormons and the local Indians, the federal government sent investigators into the area to evaluate the situation. Special Agent H. S. Welton recommended that the Paiute be given title to the areas with freshwater springs they were still cultivating in the Moencopi Wash region. But his recommendations were never put into effect, and the Paiute later lost one of these sites.

Between 1859 and 1868, the Paiute began to face a new threat to their shrinking resources. During those years, the U.S. government was engaged in several wars with the Paiute Indians' neighbors to the east—the Navajo. In order to escape the fighting, groups of Navajo looking for safety scattered throughout San Juan territory. At the close of the war, in 1868, the Navajo were granted a reservation on the New Mexico–Arizona border directly east of the San Juan Paiute homeland. The Navajo, whose population grew rapidly after the war, soon moved off their reservation in large numbers. Many of them eventually settled in San

Five members of a Paiute tribal council, their Mormon associates (men with beards), and trader S. S. Preston (far left) photographed in 1907 in Tuba City, Arizona.

Juan Paiute territory, west of the Navajo reservation. These Navajo, herding large flocks of sheep and goats over San Juan Paiute land, became the most serious competitors for the native Indians' resources.

In about 1900, the Tuba City/Moencopi area was removed from the public domain and made a part of the Western Navajo Reservation. The federal government also bought out the Mormons properties and improvements. These buildings formed the basis of the Western Navajo Agency and school.

The San Juan Paiute, like the other Paiute bands, had to alter their economy drastically in order to survive in this changed world. Because livestock had destroyed most of the wild seeds the Paiute had earlier gathered, they intensified their cultivation of their remaining farmlands. As hunting depleted the large game animal population, the Indians began to herd sheep and goats to provide themselves with meat. The Paiute also began to create items for sale. Basketmaking became an increasingly important livelihood in the 19th and 20th centuries. At non-Indian trading posts, the San Juan Paiute women exchanged their baskets for flour, sugar, coffee, and many other goods. They also traded baskets to the Navajo for sheep and goats.

The San Juan Paiute were the only Paiute group that was able to remain self-sufficient throughout the 19th century. Their culture had altered significantly, but it had managed to survive. However, in the 20th century, the San Juan Paiute, too, would face major threats to their way of life. ▲

A Moapa Paiute woman wearing a traditional basketry hat, photographed by anthropologist Robert Lowie in 1915.

PERSISTENCE AND CHANGE

At the beginning of the 20th century, the only land to which any of the Paiute bands held title was the tiny and inadequate Moapa reservation. Although the Paiute bands still inhabited portions of their traditional homelands, few of them had any control over these properties. One exception was the San Juan Paiute, who still held important sections of their traditional land in spite of Mormon and Navajo encroachment. By 1900, most of the traditional Paiute land outside of the San Juan region had been taken over by non-Indians—such as the Mormons—or by federal or state governments.

During the first several decades of the century, the federal government set aside small reservations for several Paiute groups. However, these properties were not intended to compensate the groups for what they had lost nor, in most cases, were they sufficient to provide for the groups' subsistence. They were merely supposed to provide land on which the Paiute could build their homes so that they would not live as squatters.

The Mormon settlers in Utah and Arizona were generally more supportive of the federal government's decision to give the Paiute land than were the non-Mormon settlers in Nevada. For instance, in the early 1900s, the Mormons were instrumental in the creation of a reservation for the Shivwits Paiute band. In 1903, Anthony W. Ivins, a rancher and mayor of the Mormon town of St. George, purchased a small piece of land on the Santa Clara River, as well as several pieces of farming equipment, for these Indians to use. He then obtained authorization from the federal government to move the approximately 150 Shivwits onto the tract. The land was then purchased by the U.S. government and officially designated as a federal reservation.

Ivins and the other townspeople justified the removal of the Shivwits by claiming that the Indians' quality of life would improve at the reservation. The Mormons argued that if the Shivwits there could be taught non-Indian—and in the Mormons' opinion, better—farming techniques and receive schooling, they would prosper. In actuality, the Mormons in the region were motivated

A brush shelter belonging to a Shivwits Paiute family in 1915. Shelters such as this were used only during warm seasons.

to a great extent by their desire for the Shivwits people's land. The Shivwits Paiute had survived relatively unmolested until the late 1880s because of the isolation of their homeland. But when Mormon ranchers began moving into Shivwits territory and the Indians began raiding their cattle, conflict between the two groups arose. It was therefore to the Mormons' advantage to remove the Shivwits from the area they had settled to a smaller, less valuable parcel. The new reservation included only about 70 acres of tillable land. As a result, the relocated Indians were forced to depend on sporadic wage-work in the Mormon community in order to make a living.

In 1907, the federal government established reservations for two other Paiute bands—the Kaibab and the San Juan. These actions were prompted by Laura Work, superintendent of the school in Panguitch, Utah. In 1905, Work sent a letter to the commissioner of Indian Affairs "concerning the condition of the Kaibab and San Juan Indians, two bands of Paiute in southern Utah." In response, the government sponsored two fact-finding trips to the region. On October 16, 1907, after examining the results of the inspections, the Department of the Interior created the reservations by departmental order.

The Kaibab and San Juan Paiute bands were living in circumstances very different from each other at the time their reservations were established. The Kaibab were living as squatters (illegal settlers) on what was formerly their own territory. They supported themselves through a combination of hunting and gathering the area's depleted plant and animal resources, working at low-paying wage jobs in Mormon villages and farms, and even begging for work or food when necessary. The San Juan Paiute, on the other hand, had retained effective control over much of their most valuable land. In particular, they had held on to their farms at Willow Springs and Paiute Canyon.

The Kaibab Paiute reservation was established south of the Utah-Arizona border, in their traditional territory. It was enlarged in 1913 and again in 1917 to its present size of 120,413 acres. According to Kaibab Paiute Mabel Drye, who was a schoolgirl at the time of the reservation discussions, federal officials at first suggested that the Kaibab be placed on the same reservation as the San Juan Paiute. The Kaibab had not wished to move in the 19th century, and they were no more interested in the prospect this time. The local Mormons supported the Kaibab band's wish to remain in their ancestral lands and successfully prevented their removal. Drye explained:

> [A] government man gathered them [the Paiute] in town to talk to them. The Mormons were there listening. He had gathered to talk to them. He was asking them if they would like to move to an area around Glendale [Utah] or Johnson [Utah] or Kanab [Utah]. The Indian people said that they didn't like Glendale—it was just a big wash—and at Johnson nothing

> grew good. "And how about Kanab?" he asked. We said, "No." I don't know where we would've been placed. . . . The government man said that if we didn't like any of these areas, they were going to send us to San Juan. And then a lot of the Mormons got together and talked among themselves and then told the man, "How could they be moved? They are O.K. where they are." Then Wari said that she wasn't going to move. She was going to stay near her graveyard. Her father, Captain Frank, was buried there. The government man got real mad because he wanted to send them to San Juan, but the Mormons were the ones that prevented him from doing that.

Although the Kaibab clearly appreciated their neighbors' help, the Mormons did not give up the best land to the Indians. The reservation did not include the areas where the major springs are located. One of these water sources, Moccasin Spring, is located in the center of the reservation, but it was not included in the land grant and today continues to be the site of a small Mormon farming village. The Mormons agreed even before the reservation was established to give the Kaibab one-third of the flow of the spring, but many Paiute felt, as they do still, that they should have received title to the spring and the land surrounding it.

Mabel Drye was also present when the reservation was officially established. She described the situation to the authors of this book and to Kaibab Paiute Lucille Jake.

> I remember when Kaibab was made into a reservation. There was a lady and a man and the lady wasn't married. She was the boss. A man was helping her and was hauling everything, material, flour, and even yarn and needles to make stockings with. It was by the house in Moccasin where they stored all that stuff. There was a whole stack of flour, and stockings, and she was giving us material to make dresses with. Then they gave material to the men to make pants with. They gave us some stuff and our wagon got filled. We loaded all the stuff in our wagon. Also, they gave us bacon, great big thick ones. There wasn't any meat on it. The Indians said it wasn't pig meat, it must be elephant meat—it was too big. The people with more children received more food. They even gave the children bacon, and needles and thread. Then they asked the Mormons to make us stockings.

The government established the San Juan Paiute reservation in an area known as the Paiute Strip. This tract, which ran along the northern edge of the Western Navajo Reservation, was located between the San Juan River and the Utah-Arizona border. The San Juan Paiute were not provided with a federal agency of their own. Instead, they, like the Navajo and Hopi, were placed under the jurisdiction of the Western Navajo Agency on the Western Navajo

A 1920 photograph of the home of a Kaibab family, located near the Kaibab Agency at Moccasin, Arizona. In this period, most Kaibab families lived in houses like those of their Mormon neighbors.

Reservation, which had been established in 1901. The portion of the Western Navajo Reservation on which the San Juan lived was never specifically designated solely for their use. As a result, the San Juan had to compete with the Navajo for use of that territory. Stephen Janus, the federal government's representative at the Western Navajo Agency, visited three San Juan communities in 1909 and recommended that the government give them sheep and goats to aid their transition to reservation life. However, there are no records indicating that any livestock or any supplies such as those received by the Kaibab were ever received by the San Juan.

The Paiute Strip remained a Paiute reservation for only a brief time. In 1921, Leroy A. Wilson of the Paradise Oil and Refining Company wrote a series of letters to the commissioner of the Bureau of Indian Affairs (BIA), a federal office within the Department of the Interior that deals with Indian issues, requesting a permit to drill in the region. He was told that because the Paiute Strip was an Indian reservation, he could only get a drilling permit if the land was returned to the public domain. The BIA was at the time under the jurisdiction of Secretary of the Interior Albert Fall. Fall was later sentenced to prison for his unethical practices in what became known as the Teapot Dome scandal, in which he pursued a policy of opening public land to wholesale exploitation by oil and mineral companies by providing them with unauthorized and improperly awarded leases. Under Fall's instructions, the BIA officials reported falsely that the San Juan Paiute were not using their reservation. In July 1922, the Paiute Strip was returned to the public domain.

Immediately following this action, individual Navajos and officials of the newly organized Navajo Tribal Council, as well as BIA officials, began campaigning to have the Paiute Strip added to the Navajo reservation. In their arguments, the Navajo stated that "Indians" had used the land from time immemorial and that therefore it should be returned to the Navajo Indian Reservation. The "Indians" who truly owned the territory—the Paiute—were rarely mentioned in the debate that followed. In 1933, the Paiute Strip was added to the Navajo Indian Reservation.

The San Juan Paiute continued to live on the Paiute Strip and on their traditional land within the western portion of the Navajo reservation. They continued to farm, raise livestock, hunt game, gather wild foods, and sell or trade their baskets. And although they were able to hold on to sections of their traditional territory, they were steadily losing out in their competition for land with the numerous Navajo. The San Juan, who were often described as impoverished when compared to their very poor Navajo neighbors, suffered greatly during this time. Between 1900 and 1930, the San Juan Paiute population dropped from approximately 300 to about 80 and would continue to decline into the 1940s.

In 1935, the San Juan Paiute band's social and economic situation suffered a serious setback. At this time, the U.S. government consolidated the six separately administered Navajo agencies into one centralized agency. The new agency was located in the town of Window Rock on the eastern side of the Navajo reservation, far from the San Juan Paiute area. In the past, the Western Navajo Agency and the federal government had provided few services to and taken little notice of the San Juan. After the consolidation, they completely neglected these Paiute, resulting in serious problems for the Indians.

(continued on page 73)

THE WEAVING OF HISTORY

Basketmaking has always held an important place in Paiute culture. For hundreds of years, the Indians have passed down the techniques used to make the baskets and other tools necessary for day-to-day survival. However, the purpose of this craft and the use of its products has changed several times throughout the Paiutes' long history as a people.

Traditionally, Paiute women created many of their everyday tools using basketmaking techniques and materials. They wove flat seed beaters for knocking seeds from trees and grasses, large burden baskets for carrying gathered foods, and watertight jars for storing seeds and liquids.

When the Paiute began to have steady contact with European and American settlers in the early 1800s, they gradually replaced their traditional tools with those of the settlers. The Indians did not, however, stop making baskets. They discovered that Paiute baskets were a useful commodity with which to trade for European and American goods.

The Paiute also discovered a market for their baskets among other Indian tribes. The best example is their dealings with the Navajo, for whom the San Juan Paiute make special baskets used in wedding ceremonies. The Navajo wedding basket is now the most common type made by Paiute basket makers. Thus, the Paiute have been able to adapt an age-old tradition into a lucrative 20th-century enterprise.

An early-20th-century wedding basket with traditional decoration.

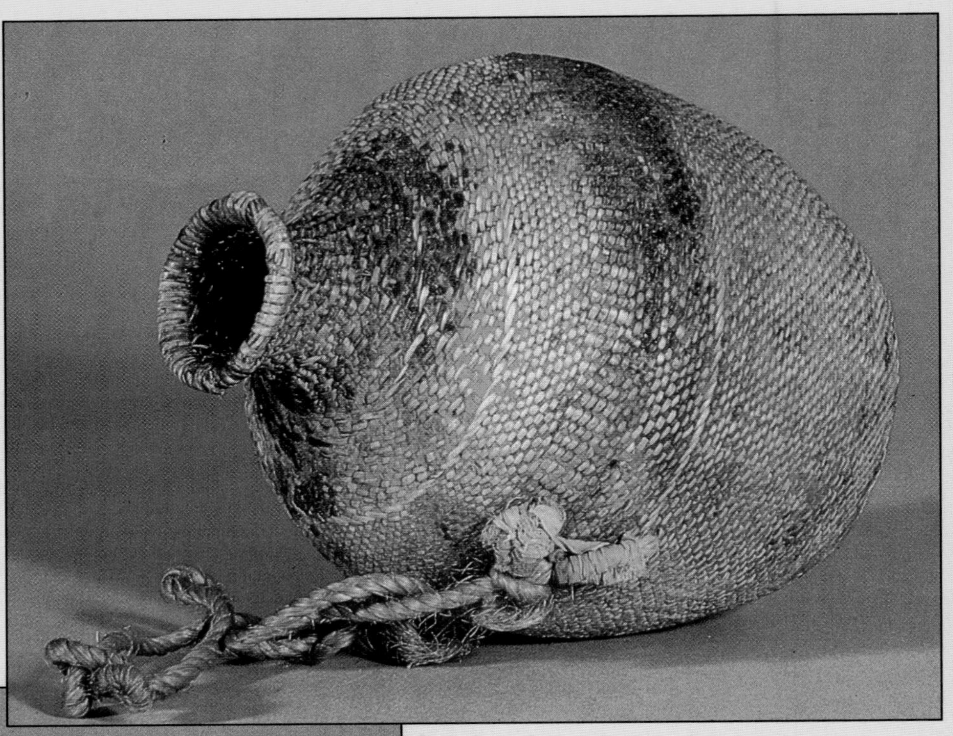

A Paiute basketry "bottle," or jug. The outside of this jug was covered with red clay and pine pitch in order to make it waterproof. It could then be used for carrying and storing liquids.

An early-20th-century Paiute jug, known as a bottle basket. The striped pattern was created by interweaving several twines made from willow, redbud, and juniper bark. Bottles such as this were used for storing seeds.

A burden basket made in 1982 by San Juan Paiute weaver Grace Lehi.
The basket was fashioned by coiling bundles of yucca fiber into a conical shape.

San Juan Paiute weavers have made distinctive Navajo wedding baskets since the late 1800s. Traditionally, these baskets were decorated with a simple circle of points. However, modern Paiute weavers have adapted many different designs into their work, including variations on the circle, designs from other tribes, and original patterns from the weavers' own imagination. Today, San Juan craftspeople are building a better future for their tribe through the money raised by their basket cooperative—the San Juan Southern Paiute Yingup Weavers Association.

A 1984 wedding basket, made by San Juan Paiute Grace Lehi.

This cogwheel design was created using strands of sumac and brown willow twine.

The crosses on this basket represent a legendary Navajo deity, Spider Woman.

A basket woven in 1984 by Rose Ann Whiskers of Hidden Springs.

A 1984 wedding basket decorated with butterflies and bees.

This intricately woven basket features black and red horses.

San Juan Paiute weaver Marilu Lehi created this basket after being inspired by spring butterflies.

This basket is decorated with a Navajo "squash blossom" design.

A variation on the traditional circle of points, created in 1984 by Rose Ann Whiskers.

(continued from page 64)

The Paiute bands living in Nevada did not fare any better than those in Arizona and Utah. Aside from the Moapa Paiute reservation, the only land set aside for the Paiute in Nevada was a 10-acre tract in Las Vegas. In December 1911, Helen J. Stewart had deeded the land "for the use of the Paiute Indians." An account in the January 6, 1912, edition of the *Las Vegas Age* reported that the Federal Indian Agency had bought the land from Stewart. The report commented that "Mrs. Stewart has always been a good friend of the Indians and it is very desirable that their permanent home should be so located as to bring them within her influence and control." Las Vegas Paiute Daisy Mike, a six year old in 1912, noted that

> the reason why Helen J. Stewart gave this Colony to the Indians is that we wandered around here and there and didn't have a place of our own, or a reservation. So she willed this ten acres of land to us Southern Paiutes.

Soon after this, the agent for the Paiute in southern Nevada moved the agency from Moapa, where there had been a full-time agent since 1903, to more centrally located Las Vegas to better serve the Nevada Paiute. But in 1918, the agent again returned the agency to Moapa after reporting that there was not enough land or money available to purchase a larger reservation for the Las Vegas Paiute.

After the agency headquarters returned to Moapa, some Paiute continued to live on the land granted to them in Las Vegas, but they were largely left to their own devices. Agent L. B. Sandall of the Moapa agency described the Las Vegas Paiute in 1926.

> On the small Reservation of ten acres near Las Vegas, there are about fifty Indians who make it their headquarters, some living there permanently. They have no tillable land and are all self supporting by labor in and around Las Vegas, the women washing and doing domestic work; the men doing ordinary labor by the day on the ranches. All the Indians in the surrounding country who visit this section make this small Reservation their headquarters, thus giving this small Reservation a very fluctuating population.

Life on the Moapa reservation was very difficult during the early decades of the 20th century. Outbreaks of disease, particularly tuberculosis, continued to cause sharp population declines. Although many of the Moapa Paiute attempted to farm, several factors worked against them. Local non-Indian ranchers allowed their cattle to invade the Indians' farmland, and periodic floods and an insufficient amount of tillable land resulted in little or no profits. As a result, many Moapa Paiute continued to work for local ranchers and farmers in order to survive.

Other Paiute bands in Nevada, such as the Pahrump living to the west of Las Vegas, received no reservation land at all. They supported themselves al-

San Juan Paiute Jo-De (left) with Western Navajo agent M. M. Murphy in Tuba City, Arizona, in 1907.

most entirely by performing wagework for the local non-Indian population. Some of them eventually moved onto the Las Vegas or the Moapa reservation, but others remained separate.

In Utah, a 1915 executive order created a reservation for those Utah Paiute who became known as the Indian Peaks Band. This tract was located in southwestern Utah about 25 miles north of Modena, Utah, near the Nevada border. A non-Indian settler, Calvin Connell, remembered a visit to the area in the early 1920s:

> In 1923, winter of 1923, I went into Pine Valley, Beaver County and came in contact with the old Indian village out there, Indian Peak, an old Indian village. So quite a number of Indians there at that time. . . . I used to see them quite a lot the Indians, they'd come down, look around, and they'd associate with us and swap things [and] we used to kind of help them out in that respect, for food and stuff.

The Paiute at Indian Peaks lived in a small number of log cabins and supported themselves with gardens, piñon pine nuts, and a few cattle. By the mid-1930s, however, most had moved away to Cedar City, where they lived with the Cedar Paiute Band. Most supported themselves with wagework, supplemented by hunting and gathering in season on their reservation land.

Although federal funds were appropriated in 1899 and 1925 to purchase land for the Cedar City Paiute, this money was never spent. The failure to use the 1925 appropriation appears to have been caused by a misunderstanding between the federal government and the Mormon church. Apparently believing that the federal government was not going to do anything for the Paiute, Mormon church officials bought the Indians 10 acres north of the city. Federal officials heard of the Mormon church's actions and decided not to spend the federal funds. As a result, the Cedar City Paiute never received lands held in trust for them by the federal government. Because of their lack of trust lands, these Paiute were later considered ineligible for the meager federal support when it finally became available.

In the early 20th century, two final reservations were given to Paiute bands in Utah. These were the Koosharem Reservation, near Richfield, in 1928, and the Kanosh Reservation, near Kanosh, in 1929. Because the Koosharem Reservation was isolated, most of the Koosharem Paiute eventually relocated to the town of Richfield, where the Mormon church gave them use of a plot of land on the edge of town. Individual Paiute in both groups had also been given allotments of land earlier by the federal government and were supporting themselves in part by farming.

During the early 1900s, Paiute children received very sporadic educations. There were government-run day schools located at Kaibab, Shivwits, Moapa, and Las Vegas for lengths of time ranging from about 30 years for the Kaibab school to only 1 year for the Las Vegas school. When there were no schools located among the Paiute bands, children were generally sent away to boarding schools and, in later years, to public schools.

For a few years between 1900 and 1910, some Paiute children were sent to the Panguitch School. Mabel Drye, who

Philanthropist Helen J. Stewart, photographed in the 1910s with her collection of Paiute baskets. Stewart donated a small parcel of land for what became known as the Las Vegas colony of Paiute Indians.

was a student there during its brief existence, recalled the Panguitch School:

> And then when I got a little older they sent me to school. There was a school going on there in Panguitch. My brother and I were sent there. I'm telling all about myself and my brother. That's where I spent my days learning to read and write in English. And then every summer we went home. My grandfather used to send the horses so we could come home. Then my brother and I used to ride on one horse. Some of the children had to stay at school all the time and not come home because they kept doing things wrong and acting bad, like kids are doing today. So they stayed there all summer. Now isn't the only time they're doing that running around; they've been doing that a long time but we [my brother and I] always came home.

A small number of San Juan Paiute children attended a boarding school in Tuba City, Arizona, on the Navajo reservation. However, most San Juan children did not attend any school at all during the early 1900s.

Many Indian boarding schools, such as Sherman in California and Stewart in Nevada, were located far away from Paiute territory. As a result, the homes of many Pauite children who were sent to them were so far away that these students had to stay at the schools during the summer recess. Paiute children generally remained at these schools for several years, living with white people and working for them during summer vacation.

Boarding schools were very strict. Indian children were forbidden to speak their native languages and were punished if they did. Some children ran away, and although a few made it home, most were caught and punished. And many died from diseases caught at school. After graduation, Indian children sometimes stayed in the towns where they had attended school to work for a while. Some never returned to the reservation or came back only occasionally to visit friends or relatives.

Throughout the 20th century, many Paiute of all ages continued to die from disease. This was especially true during the early decades. Many diseases, including tuberculosis, whooping cough, measles, typhoid, and influenza, and especially the devastating 1918 "Spanish Influenza," killed a great number of Paiute. Officials reported that Paiute children were especially susceptible, but many young adults died as well. Not until the 1930s, and in some areas not until even the 1950s, did the Paiute communities begin to have more births than deaths during a given year. After 1950, the Paiute population again began to slowly increase.

In this period, the Paiute had to adapt themselves to the economic environment of mainstream America as best they could. They worked on ranches as cowboys or domestics and were employed by railroad companies. For the most part, however, the Paiute were an underemployed pool of un-

LOCATION OF PAIUTE RESERVATIONS TODAY

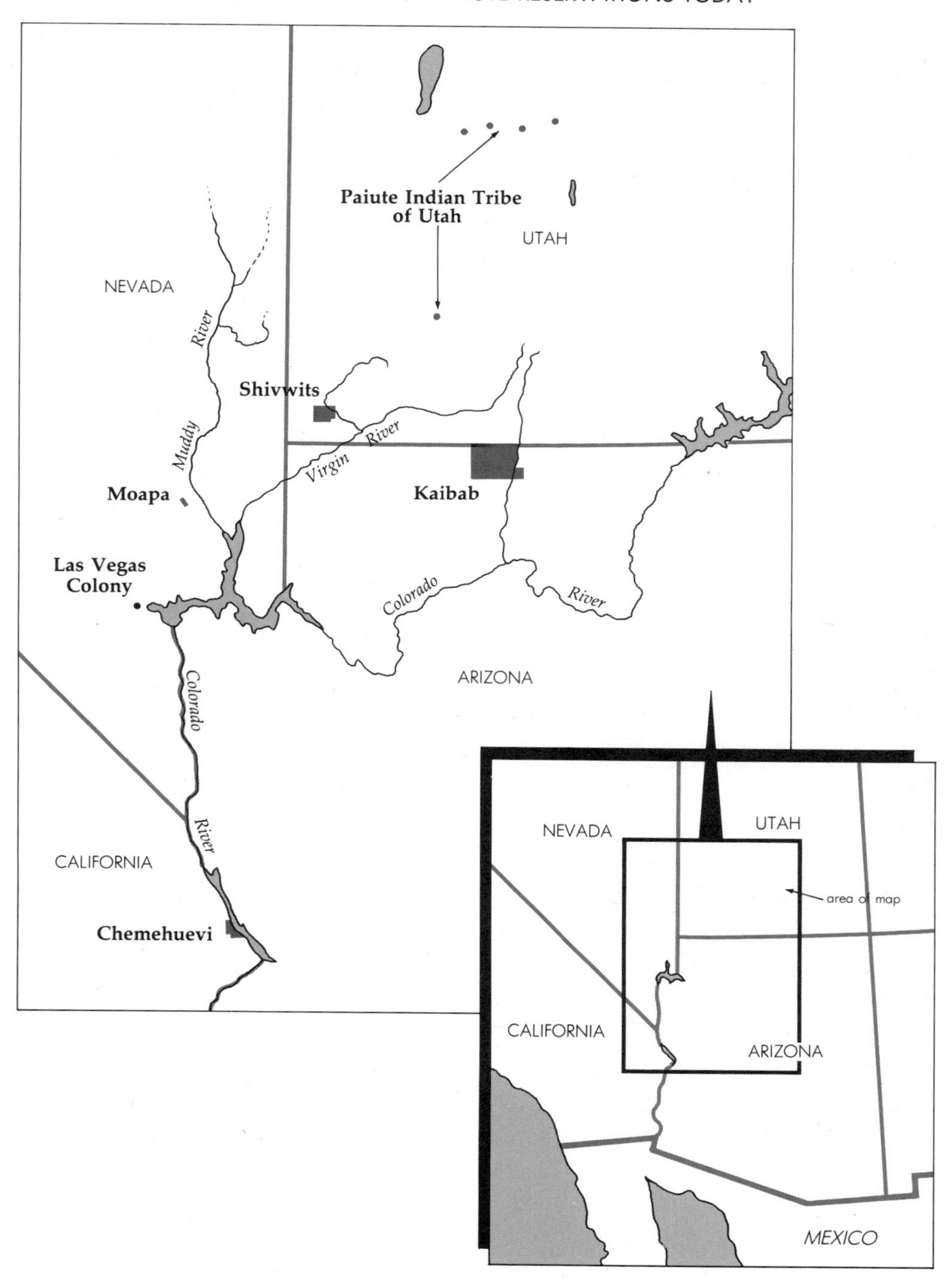

skilled rural labor, often hired by others to harvest produce from lands the Indians themselves once farmed. In the 1940s and 1950s, there were networks among members of different bands providing information about farm labor jobs. For example, in 1946, Joe Pikyavit, a Paiute living in Kanosh, Utah, wrote to Alfred Lehi, the spokesperson of the San Juan band, regarding arrangements for work with Utah Mormon farmers.

Well into the 20th century, the Paiute continued to hunt and to gather traditional food and medicinal plants even though these resources were very much depleted. In most cases, the Indians were forced to collect the foods and medicines because they could not afford to pay for them in the non-Indian communities. Many Paiute continued to make traditional crafts, such as buckskin and baskets. Although some were produced for private use, most were sold to traders or tourists for very low prices. Even though the craftspeople were underpaid, the small amounts of

Indian pupils in front of one of the buildings at the Bureau of Indian Affairs school in Panguitch, Utah, in 1907.

cash or goods they received were essential to the survival of their families.

Many other aspects of traditional Paiute life persisted into the mid-20th century. Whenever Paiute groups gathered together for social, economic, or religious reasons, they continued to perform round dances, sing songs, tell traditional stories, and play gambling games. Many of them also performed traditional rituals at puberty, birth, and death. Of course, the Paiute were also influenced by their non-Indian neighbors. They adopted some non-Paiute religious activities—such as the rituals of the Mormon and other Christian churches. The Indians also adopted some of their neighbors' social pastimes—such as non Indian card games. In the late 19th century, the Paiute adopted the Yaxap, or Cry, funerary ceremony from the Mojave and other Yuman-speaking tribes living to the south. The Las Vegas Paiute may have even adopted this ceremony in the era before white settlement. In the Cry, singers chant songs from evening until dawn over the course of one or more nights. Each song is part of several sacred song cycles, including the salt song cycle and the bird song cycle. The song cycles are meant to sing the spirit of the deceased along a special route through traditional Paiute land to his or her dwelling place in the next world. Between periods of singing, relatives and friends get up and give speeches about the deceased. When it was first adopted, the Cry ceremony was separate from traditional Paiute funeral ceremonies. In time, however, the Cry became part of the individual funeral ceremony.

The Paiute had received only a minuscule amount of financial help from the federal government before the 1950s. In 1954, even that small amount was taken away from the four Utah Paiute bands with reservations. At this time, the U.S. Congress voted to "terminate" the federal recognition of the Paiute bands. During the 1950s, the U.S. government sought to terminate, or end, its official relationship with several Indian tribes, including the Menominee of Wisconsin, the Klamath of Oregon, and several of the Paiute bands. When a tribe was terminated, the government stopped supervising its reservation land, and federal services to the tribe members ceased. Also, the Indians and their property came under the jurisdiction of the government of the state in which they lived.

This policy, which was in effect from the early 1950s until 1970, was theoretically applicable only to those tribes that were considered able to participate successfully on their own in the mainstream American economy. But this was clearly not the case with the Utah Paiute. During congressional termination hearings, the Indians were reported to be in poor economic condition. They had a high rate of illiteracy, a low level of education, and low family incomes (the average annual income in 1968 was $2,746), and most lived in substandard housing. Nevertheless, in 1957, the Utah Paiute were terminated even though Congress was aware that the Indian group did not meet the government's own standards for termination.

When the Utah Paiute's termination went into effect, they had to begin paying state taxes on their land for the first time. Within 10 years, the Kanosh and Koosharem bands of Paiute lost much of their land through nonpayment, and the Indian Peaks Paiute sold their reservation to avoid being taxed. The Shivwits Paiute were able to retain ownership of their land only by leasing it to non-Paiute to raise the needed tax money. Termination also ended the rights of the four bands to federal health programs and other social services.

Ironically, the Cedar City band was not terminated because it had been denied federal reservation land. These Paiute consequently continued to receive certain services. Although they had earlier been denied many social services, they were now allowed some federal services precisely because they had no land to lose.

In 1965, the fortunes of the Paiute tribes began to change for the better. During that year, the Paiute were awarded a court judgment of $7,253,165.19. This judgment resulted from a federal court case in which the Paiute claimed that their traditional lands had been taken without just payment. The Paiute had filed their claim with the Indian Claims Commission, which was created in 1946 by an act of Congress. Under the terms of the act, Indian groups that believed the federal government had illegally taken their lands or had otherwise treated them unjustly could bring their claims before a special three-judge court commission. If the tribes were able to convince the federal judges that they had valid complaints, the government awarded the tribes a monetary judgment.

Before dividing and distributing the money awarded to the Paiute, the federal government had to determine how many Paiute were entitled to a portion of it. For this purpose, the government began to compile a roll that would list the name of every Paiute. In addition to the Paiute already enrolled in recognized tribes, the roll also included people who were members of unrecognized tribes. The greater the number of Paiute enrolled, the smaller the amount each person would receive. It is therefore significant that a party of Paiute from Kaibab and the various terminated Utah bands went to the San Juan community to make sure that eligible San Juan Paiute were enrolled. In a feature article that appeared in the *Flagstaff Sun* on July 14, 1970, journalist Jeff Stone described their meetings:

> Castro [Ralph Castro, a Kaibab Paiute] began, with help from the Kaibab band, an effort to get Paiute on the Navajo Reservation included on the roll for the federal judgment.
>
> Paiutes from the Kaibab Reservation, the Cedar City [Utah], Kanarsh [Kanosh] and St. George areas, pooled money for gasoline and

came to the Navajo Reservation to
seek their relatives.

The incoming Paiutes talked and
questioned those who came forward.
Many common ancestors were
discovered, family histories
compared. When the process was
completed, 98 were sufficiently
identified of Paiute ancestors to
qualify for the judgment, even though
the share of each established Paiute
was diminished as each new name
was added.

In the end, the government gave each member of the Paiute bands without special trust lands a cash award of $7,522. The money due to the Paiute groups that had kept their reservations was given to their tribal councils, which then voted on how to distribute the

Moapa Paiutes Eugene and Dalton Tom, photographed in the 1950s on the Moapa reservation in Nevada.

Luella Tom standing on one of the roads on the Moapa reservation in Nevada, photographed in June 1962.

funds. Both the Moapa and Kaibab tribes voted to allocate a significant proportion of their awards to tribal economic and social development rather than give all the money to individuals. As a result, these bands were able to turn around their economies. For example, the members of the Moapa band started a commercial farming operation using an outlay of funds from the judgment award. They were later able to finance improvements in the operation through a series of federal grants.

The groups that distributed their funds in individual payments received far fewer long-term benefits. Some individuals were able to use the money to improve their housing or invest in livestock, but for many Paiute, the $7,522 went very quickly. The amount was simply not enough to significantly improve the very poor economic situation of most of the Paiute.

During the 1970s, the five bands of Utah Paiute formed a legal corporation. They worked together on a number of projects, even managing to get a government grant of $491,999 to build several multipurpose buildings designed to house small industries in Cedar City, Richfield, and Kanosh. Most importantly, they convinced the federal government to restore its trust relationship with the Shivwits, Kanosh, Koosharem, and Indian Peaks bands. Congress finally became aware that termination had not been an appropriate solution to the economic and social problems of the Utah Paiute. On April 3, 1980, the Paiute Indian Tribe of Utah Restoration Act was passed. This act restored the four terminated bands as a formally recognized Indian group and confirmed the trust status of the Cedar City band. It also united the five Utah bands into the Paiute Indian Tribe of Utah. Under the provisions of the act, each band kept its own government but sent a representative to a tribal council that had jurisdiction over all five bands. A plan to acquire 15,000 acres of reservation land for the tribe was also included. This last provision resulted in a great deal of controversy with the local non-Paiute residents and with federal officials. The Utah Paiute eventually ended up with title to a number of parcels of land that totaled 4,770 acres. They also sought to obtain some tracts owned by the Forest Service but were unable to do so.

During this era, the San Juan Paiute tribe was working to get official federal recognition as a tribe from the U.S. government. Although they had never been officially terminated, the San Juan Paiute had for all practical purposes lost their tribal status after the consolidation of the various Navajo agencies. Because they were not terminated, they decided to seek recognition through the BIA rather than the court system used by the Utah Paiute. The San Juan formally petitioned the BIA for recognition in 1980, and their petition received preliminary approval for recognition in 1987. On December 11, 1989, the BIA and the Department of the Interior gave their final approval: The San Juan were at last a recognized tribe. In addition to the recognition process, the San Juan Paiute have also been involved throughout most of the 1980s in a land claims lawsuit with the Navajo and Hopi tribes. The claims include lands that the San Juan Paiute still use as well as land that was lost during the 1930s.

Members of the San Juan Paiute band gather sumac for basketmaking.

Each band of Paiute has had its own unique history. As a result, these groups today remain distinct from one another in many ways. For example, the Kaibab have adopted many of the external characteristics of mainstream American culture, but the core of their life remains distinctly Paiute. The San Juan, however, have until recently remained relatively isolated from mainstream American influences. All the Paiute bands have been faced with attempts by non-Indians to change or destroy their Indian culture, but they have fought these threats in varying ways and with varying degrees of success. ▲

Dan Bullets, an important Kaibab Paiute elder, photographed in 1981 in the traditional Kaibab territory of southern Utah.

KAIBAB: A MODERN COMMUNITY

The victory of the Paiute in their claims against the United States in 1965 afforded many bands an opportunity to turn their fortunes around. The Kaibab, in particular, implemented a very successful economic and social revival.

The Kaibab population has approximately doubled since the late 1960s. More than 200 are now enrolled in the tribe. Approximately 100 Kaibab Paiute live on the band's 200-square-mile reservation, which is located on the border of Utah and Arizona in the center of traditional Kaibab territory. Ancient red sandstone cliffs form a backdrop for what has become a very modern-looking community. The tribe has begun the construction of several new housing developments, a modern tribal office building, and a new multipurpose community center. It has also expanded social services and increased the number of jobs available to its tribe members. The Kaibab band's prosperity has been aided by allocating 70 percent of the award to different tribal programs, including education, community development, administration, and tribal business enterprises. Another 15 percent of the judgment was allocated in individual payments to each tribe member. The remaining money was placed in a special fund that was used to help families pay off their debts and make needed purchases. The tribe also received a number of federal grants for projects ranging from housing and educational programs to the construction of a tourist area.

The Kaibab Paiute have adjusted to many aspects of modern American life, but they have also kept a strong identity as Paiute. On the surface, they appear at times to share many aspects of mainstream U.S. culture, but they still retain uniquely Paiute attitudes, values, and behavior in all aspects of their daily life. Their methods of interaction and communication, relations among families and larger groups, and patterns of leadership are all consistent with traditional Paiute beliefs and behavior.

More obvious aspects of Paiute culture are also present on the reservation. Although English is now the predominant language spoken, the Southern Paiute language is still common. Middle-aged and elderly tribe members often speak Paiute to each other or sometimes sprinkle Paiute words or phrases in their conversation. Younger Paiute have some familiarity with the language and most of them know at least a few words.

Traditional Paiute crafts and ceremonies still play an important role in daily reservation life. Many Kaibab are known for their buckskin work, beading, and other crafts. They still dance the traditional round dance and bear dance, and many of the younger members dance at Indian powwows with members of other tribes. The Kaibab also sing the traditional mourning songs as part of the Cry ceremony during funerals, often traveling to different Paiute tribes for these ceremonies.

At present, the Cry ceremony lasts one or two nights and consists of one or two song cycles sung by groups of singers led by a ritual specialist. During the pauses between songs, the mourners get up and speak of their grief for the deceased, talk about what they believe that person stood for, and thank those who are present for paying their respects and giving their sympathy. Cake and coffee are served at midnight during a break in the ceremony, and after the last song ends at daybreak the participants all breakfast together. Often a Christian or Mormon church ceremony follows the traditional Paiute one.

The Kaibab's program to create more housing on the reservation is another example of their ability to combine successfully their traditions with modern practices. Even when the amount of housing is limited, the Kaibab's traditional kinship system provides them with a wide variety of options about where to live. When a couple and their children cannot obtain their own house, they may choose to move in with members of either the husband's or the wife's family. The parents of the husband or wife, or even their cousins, aunts, or uncles, would welcome the family into their home. The availability of housing on the reservation increased during the 1970s and 1980s, allowing extended families to separate into smaller units, but the strong economic and social ties between the families continue. New housing and the increasing number of jobs have also helped to bring back many tribe members who had earlier moved away.

Even though new housing developments have given the reservation communities a surface resemblance to many non-Indian communities, traditional Paiute patterns of social interaction persist. The Kaibab generally socialize with relatives rather than with neighbors. Family members, especially children and young adults, frequently shift residences among various related households. For example, a Paiute child might ask to leave his or her parents' home and move in with an aunt's family. In Paiute society, this is not considered surprising, and the request is generally respected. In some cases, entire households have switched homes one or more times with other related households.

Most Kaibab Paiute marry either other Kaibab Paiute or members of one of the other Paiute groups. As a result, Kaibab Paiute often have the option of choosing to live on the Kaibab reservation or with Paiute kin in another community. However, these choices are not permanent, and many Paiute

Kaibab Paiute Lucille Jake and her granddaughter wringing out a piece of buckskin as part of the tanning process, photographed in 1987. The Kaibab continue to make buckskin products for commercial sale.

move back and forth several times between communities as their circumstances change.

In 1934, the Kaibab Paiute Tribe, like many other American Indian tribes, adopted a written constitution at the suggestion of the U.S. government. The constitution provides for a tribal manager and an elected chairperson, who are full-time employees of the tribe, as well as an elected tribal council. Tribal councils and leaders are not new among the Paiute, but their constitutional requirement that the members be elected for specific terms and by a majority vote was an innovation recommended by the BIA. The chairperson's offices, as well as those of other tribal employees, are located in a modern office building situated near the Pipe Springs National Monument, the site of an old Mormon fort. These employees see to the daily functioning of tribal affairs. However, major decisions are made by the elected tribal council at regular meetings.

Many aspects of the traditional Paiute political structure still permeate their modern-day government. For example, council members generally try to gain a consensus on a particular issue, even though the constitution only requires a majority decision. Only a small number of the adult tribal members comprise the elected council, but much of the governing is actually in the hands of several committees composed of whomever wishes to join. Elders, especially religious leaders, are active on all of these committees, but generally not on the elected council. Their moral

Houses built on the Kaibab reservation as part of the community's program to increase the availability of housing for tribe members.

Kaibab Leta Segmiller weaving traditional twined sandals in 1987.

authority and the respect given to them by the rest of the tribe lends weight to their work. In the mid-1980s, the committees were formally recognized in a revised version of the tribe's constitution. This new body of laws incorporates the committees and other traditional political practices into the official system of government.

The Kaibab band's gains in population, housing, jobs, and social services are all interrelated. They are largely based in the tribal government's expertise in applying for grants and in its effective administration. During the 1970s and 1980s, tribal officials also became skilled at dealing with the federal government, particularly with the BIA. The Kaibab began taking control over their own social services by contracting certain programs from the BIA and staffing them with tribe members. At pres-

Kaibab children practicing the steps of the traditional bear dance. Many aspects of the Kaibab's daily life resemble mainstream American culture, but they still keep many of their traditions alive.

ent, the tribe runs its own police department, senior citizen program, and medical, health, and education programs. They also have their own social service director who deals with a number of other social work issues related to the tribe's programs.

The Paiute have also successfully conducted a campaign to acquire a federal agency for their tribe. During much of the 20th century, each of the various federally recognized Paiute communities was under the jurisdiction of a different agency. These federal offices, located in several states, were often responsible for more than one tribe. For example, the Kaibab Paiute agency was also responsible for the Hopi tribe. Its office was located at the Hopi settlement of Keams Canyon, Arizona, 250 miles away from the Kaibab. Of course, the federal agent there primarily concentrated on the concerns of the large Hopi tribe, which inevitably led the Paiute to believe the agency's services were not being properly allocated. The issue was finally settled in 1982 when the U.S. government established a BIA field station at Cedar City, Utah, exclusively for the Paiute. Since the establishment of the new agency, funding and services are now distributed among groups who share a common Paiute identity. Although competition for scarce funds and services is still unavoidable, at least the Paiute groups are competing on a relatively equal footing.

The Kaibab Paiute's dealings with the federal government are sporadic, but they must interact on almost a daily basis with their neighbors in local non-Indian communities. Kaibab and non-Indians work together and attend the same schools and churches. A very few marry each other. But in spite of decades of interaction, many local non-Indians know very little about what happens on the reservation. They tend to think about the Kaibab according to long-held negative stereotypes.

Members of local Mormon communities commonly view the Kaibab in terms of their limited knowledge of the Mormons' 19th-century conquest of the region. Although some of the earliest colonizers appreciated the Paiute's knowledge, use, and management of the land and were grateful for the help the Paiute provided them, in the end they appropriated the Indians' most productive land. Consequently, the later Mormons were only aware of the Paiute as a displaced people whose livelihood had disappeared. Therefore, rather than being noted for their skilled management of natural resources, the Paiute were seen as poor, nomadic savages. This led the Mormons to assume a patronizing attitude toward the Indians when they attempted to teach them non-Indian methods of farming and other useful skills. The Mormons were willing to help the Indians if necessary, but they felt that the Paiute ought to provide for themselves despite their lack of resources.

The daily contacts between the Kaibab and the Mormons are markedly influenced by the two groups' differing views of history and the stereotypes that go with them. For Kaibab living on the reservation, contact with non-Indians usually begins in elementary school. Children living in the community of Kaibab Village or in two nearby housing clusters generally attend kindergarten through third grade at a public day school in Moccasin, a small Mormon village in the center of the reservation. For the remainder of their schooling, Kaibab children are bused 15 miles away to public schools in Fredonia, Arizona. Children who live close to Fredonia generally attend Fredonia schools for all their years of education.

At both the Moccasin and Fredonia schools, the teachers are non-Indian, and in Fredonia, Kaibab children are a decided minority. Although they tend to be enthusiastic students in early grades, especially at the Moccasin school, many soon become discouraged, and a number of them drop out before finishing high school. This is most likely because many Kaibab children feel that their culture and beliefs are not respected or understood by the non-Indian community. Incidents of prejudice and insensitivity occur fairly often. In biology class, for example, Kaibab children are sometimes made to handle human bones that were known to have been taken from Paiute burials. Also, non-Indian teachers frequently tell their Kaibab students that their traditional religious beliefs are wrong.

In 1976, the Kaibab attempted to respond to these problems by planning an innovative school on the reservation for preschool through sixth grade. Although they did not succeed, the funding proposal submitted by the tribal council to the U.S. Office of Education details the difficulties faced by Paiute children in public schools:

> The tribal government feels that they do not have adequate input into the classroom curriculum and materials and, as a result, the needs of the

> Indian children are not being met. It is clear that the public school has no intention of meeting the special educational needs of our Indian children. The non-Indian community and school board (also totally non-Indian) are especially resentful and antagonistic to our Paiute people. We do not like this resentment to affect the education of our children and are determined to change this situation. We know we have to take this into our own hands and use our imagination to develop our own Paiute curriculum utilizing our language, and culture.

In the past, a number of families sent their children to the federally run Phoenix Indian School in Phoenix, Arizona, in an attempt to circumvent the problems in the public schools. However, this school is currently being phased out and will soon no longer provide Kaibab students with an alternative to public school.

In spite of these problems, a number of Kaibab students have managed to enter institutions of higher education. Many have obtained bachelor's degrees and, in a few cases, master's degrees. The tribe hopes to keep these people on the reservation by finding appropriate employment for them. Unfortunately, the Kaibab's economy has not yet provided enough positions for these graduates. Many have had to leave the local area to find jobs in their fields. Others have stayed on the reservation, but they remain underemployed.

A number of Kaibab living on the reservation are employed by the tribe's government in managerial and clerical positions. The tribe also hires people to maintain its buildings and to run the various programs contracted from the BIA, such as the tribal agricultural project that produces grain for commercial sale. Others are employed at the local sawmill in nearby Fredonia. Tribal members also supplement their income or food supply by cultivating corn and other crops and by raising cattle and other livestock on the reservation.

The rights of Kaibab Paiute to their reservation lands and to the resources on them are another important aspect of the Indians' interaction with their local non-Paiute neighbors. Questions concerning access to water, mining for minerals, travel across the reservation, and leases for grazing lands are just a few of the issues that non-Paiute have raised at Kaibab tribal council meetings. Concerned Kaibab have also approached Mormon town governments about some of these matters. The question of who owns the right to the region's water—a major area of conflict in the arid Southwest—has given rise to formal meetings between members of the Kaibab tribe and the local non-Indian communities. At one such meeting between the Kaibab council and a Mormon delegation, both sides explained their distinct views of the history of the relationship between the two groups. To the apparent surprise of the local Mormons, the Paiute stressed their continued cultural distinctiveness as well as their long-term use of the land and water before and after the arrival of the Mormons. During the talks, the Kaibab conferred with each other in Paiute. The use of their native language was both a practical means of discussing strategy and a vehicle to emphasize their distinct Paiute identity.

The Kaibab Paiute also display their "Indianness" to non-Indians in other ways. Sporting events, such as basketball and softball, bring together Paiute and non-Paiute teams in friendly confrontations. The cultural differences of the teams may not always be overtly emphasized, but in subtle ways these differences are acknowledged (for instance, the Kaibab Bucks often play softball against the Fredonia Americans). The Kaibab's periodic tribal gatherings, at which Indian foods are served, dances are performed, and crafts are exhibited, also continue to stress the pride that the Kaibab people have for their Indian identity. ▲

Elva Drye beading moccasins at a tribal gathering in 1987.

San Juan Paiute MaryAnn Owl photographed in 1983 near Navajo Mountain, Utah, preparing a mano, or pestle, a tool used for grinding corn.

SAN JUAN: A COMMUNITY IN TRANSITION

The unique history of the San Juan people has shaped their communities in ways that have made them very different from those of other Paiute groups. Most importantly, there has never been any permanent non-Indian settlement in San Juan Paiute country. The Mormon colony that existed longest—Tuba City, Arizona—lasted only from the mid-1870s until 1904, when the U.S. government bought out the Mormons' holdings in order to make the land part of the Navajo reservation.

Officially, the San Juan came under BIA supervision in 1901, when the Western Navajo Agency was established. But on the huge expanse of the Navajo reservation, the small San Juan community remained quite isolated from mainstream American society. The government expended little effort in trying to change the San Juan people's way of life by teaching them English and non-Indian social practices. Although San Juan children are now enrolled in day schools or boarding schools on the reservation, until the early 1960s only a handful of San Juan ever had a formal education. These few had little impact on the rest of the community.

However, the San Juan Paiute have been in close contact with their Indian neighbors, the Navajo and the Hopi, for more than 120 years. Neither group has ever attempted to alter the San Juan Paiute's traditional ways. Nonetheless, the proximity of these two tribes, particularly the numerous Navajo, to the San Juan has strongly affected these Paiute's way of life, especially their economy. The San Juan Paiute's present practice of herding sheep and goats, for example, was borrowed from the Navajo and Hopi.

The San Juan employ economic strategies unlike those in any other Paiute community, past or present. But they also preserve traditional Paiute practices that have been lost or have changed drastically in other Paiute communities. This unique way of life is not static, however. Because of new tribal projects and other changes on the horizon, the San Juan Paiute today are a society in transition between the old and the new.

The San Juan Paiute Tribe today has approximately 200 members. Most live in two settlement areas on the western part of the Navajo reservation. The more southern of these is called Atatsiv, or the Sands. The name refers to the sandy, juniper-dotted plateau country northwest of Tuba City, where one group of San Juan families grazes its livestock. There, families live year-round or seasonally at sheep camps. Besides Atatsiv, this settlement also includes the San Juan's farms at Willow Springs as well as a small group of homes to the south at Hidden Springs.

The San Juan people call the northern settlement Kaivyaxaru, or the Mountain Place, after their name for nearby Navajo Mountain. The Paiute's homes and grazing areas are located primarily to the north and northeast of the mountain and to the south of Lake Powell in the area in southern Utah earlier designated as the Paiute Strip. The farms of Kaivyaxaru lie primarily in Upper Paiute Canyon in Arizona southeast of Navajo Mountain.

Culturally, the San Juan Paiute have kept a great many of the "old ways." Southern Paiute is usually spoken among the community members, and many children learn it as their first language. The San Juan are the only Paiute group that still practices the traditional rituals. For example, most young women still undergo the first menstruation ceremony and most married couples participate in the first childbirth rituals. Many older San Juan, and even some of the younger tribe members, still make morning sun prayers, build bonfires for the Thunder People in the spring, and feed the fire with scraps of food. The San Juan also still perform traditional funeral ceremonies. When a tribe member dies, the relatives of the deceased kill his or her horse and burn or otherwise dispose of the dead person's property. Unlike the Kaibab and other Paiute groups to the west, the San Juan have not adopted the Cry ceremony. The San Juan held one Cry in 1983 but have not done so again.

Since the late 1960s, most San Juan have become members of the Full Gospel church, a Pentecostal Protestant denomination that is very popular among their Navajo neighbors. But in recent years, some San Juan have sought to blend their Christianity with their traditional beliefs because they value both. For instance, their traditional burial practices are today combined with

Christian funeral services, and the dead are buried in local cemeteries.

Up until very recently, the San Juan Paiute Tribe still had a traditional government. They continued to debate and decide tribal issues in council meetings, and their government was still headed by a council-appointed chief. The current leader, Evelyn James, was chosen in this fashion and is the direct descendant of the last three tribal leaders. However, in 1980, the tribal council decided to seek federal recognition, which they received on December 11, 1989. The San Juan Paiute are now in the process of changing their governing system so that it follows the United States's official guidelines for tribal governments. The tribe has already begun the process of formalizing their traditional government by writing a tribal constitution and passing bylaws.

Angel Whiskers, father of San Juan tribal leader Evelyn James, sitting in his family's outdoor kitchen on their property at Willow Springs.

The San Juan tribe sought the help of several professionals to assist in pleading their case for official recognition. They first contacted a local non-profit legal group, DNA Legal Services, to advise them. They then hired anthropologists, including the authors of this book, to assemble historic documents and to research the evidence necessary for their acknowledgment petition. Under federal regulations, an unrecognized tribe had to supply the BIA with a complete history of the tribe and the genealogical records of all of its members.

While working on the San Juan Paiute Tribe's petition, DNA attorneys discovered that portions of the Atatsiv, including Willow Springs and the Paiute Canyon areas, might be affected by a federal lawsuit between the Hopi and Navajo tribes. The San Juan were advised to intervene in the lawsuit to prevent their lands from being awarded to either the Hopi or the Navajo.

The suit began as the result of a long-standing dispute between the two tribes over land ownership on the original Hopi reservation in Arizona. When President Chester A. Arthur created the Hopi reservation in 1882, he set aside the land "for the Hopis and such other Indians as the Secretary of the Interior sees fit to settle thereon." As the Navajo population increased, they began to move their settlements on to Hopi land, preventing them from using anything but a small portion of their original reservation. As a result, the Hopi and Navajo became engaged in decades of compromise negotiations.

In the hope of settling the dispute, in 1974 the U.S. Congress decided that the two tribes should take their case before a federal judge and have the court decide how the reservation should be divided. This same congressional act also included a provision to redivide the lands in Arizona that had been added to the Navajo reservation since 1882. The federal court reached a decision in 1977 and repartitioned the lands. The new land partitioning fueled a new series of disputes between the Hopi and the Navajo and brought the San Juan Paiute into the fray. According to the redrawn boundaries, the Hopi village Moencopi is now located within the borders of the Arizona Navajo Reservation, as are the Paiute lands at Willow Springs, Atatsiv, and Paiute Canyon.

In 1982, the San Juan tribal council decided to follow the DNA's advice. Lawyers from the Native American Rights Fund—a not-for-profit legal foundation that is run and, for the most part, staffed by American Indians—will represent the San Juan. In preparation for the court case, currently being tried in Phoenix, Arizona, the San Juan have spent several years helping their attorneys and researchers collect evidence and take testimony from tribe members in preparation for the trial.

Because the San Juan Paiute are less educated than the Hopi and Navajo and are also in the minority on the reservation, there are almost no wage-pay-

San Juan leader Evelyn James participating in an expedition to gather sumac. Sumac is the primary material used in San Juan basket manufacturing.

ing jobs available to them. A few San Juan work outside the reservation in construction or at other jobs, and one tribe member is employed by the Mormon owner of the Navajo Mountain Trading Post. But most San Juan must depend primarily on produce from farming, meat and cash from livestock herding, and cash from basketry sales for their livelihood. Because the San Juan Pauite have only recently been recognized, they receive very little financial help from the government to supplement their small incomes.

At their farms in Paiute Canyon and at Willow Springs, the San Juan have reliable sources of irrigation water and grow a number of crops and fruits, including Indian corn, squashes, melons, apricots, peaches, and grapes. With the exception of grapes, introduced by the Mormons, the cultivation of these plants was probably adopted from the Hopi Indians long ago. San Juan Paiute farmers still grow amaranth and devil's claw, crops that other Paiute traditionally cultivated. The San Juan sell some of their produce, especially apricots and other fruit, at local flea markets. Most, however, they keep for their own household use.

To the north of Navajo Mountain and on Atatsiv, the San Juan keep sheep, goats, cattle, horses, and a few donkeys. Cattle are raised primarily for sale in the marketplace; the San Juan seldom slaughter a cow for their own families. The Indians also raise horses, which are needed for rounding up cattle and for transportation in the parts of the reservation with rough terrain. Some are occasionally sold for cash. Sheep and goats are seldom sold and are usually slaughtered for meat.

In mainstream American society, farms and livestock ranches, whether they are small family concerns or large corporations, are organized as busi-

A gathering of San Juan tribal elders at a council meeting at Hidden Springs, Arizona, photographed in 1983. After the San Juan Paiute received federal recognition in December 1989, they reorganized their tribal government according to U.S. government guidelines.

nesses. Profitability is the guiding principle behind their operations. In San Juan society, however, farming is organized along the lines of traditional family relationships. Among the San Juan, there are several large extended families made up of cousins, brothers, sisters, aunts, and uncles. These family groups own their fields in common and cooperate as a group to provide food for each other rather than to earn a profit. The San Juan grow some European crops and use some modern equipment, such as irrigation tanks and pipes. But unlike farms owned by the descendants of Europeans, the kin-based organization of the San Juan's farms is much as it was in prehistoric and early historic times.

Livestock herding is not a traditional Paiute way of making a living. The Paiute's sheep, goats, cattle, horses, and donkeys were all originally introduced to the West by the Spanish in the 1600s. The Paiute acquired them secondhand from the Hopi and Navajo in the latter half of the 19th century. The techniques and tools for managing and using these animals also came indirectly from the Spanish, either by way of the Navajo and Hopi or of non-Indian cowboys hired in the 1930s and 1940s by the Navajo Agency.

Although herding is not traditional, it is governed by the same extended family relationships as farming. One San Juan custom illustrates this well. San Juan adults encourage young children to make pets of baby sheep and goats when they are born in the spring.

Marie Lehi, photographed in 1983 holding a rug she has just finished weaving. She is sitting in the Lehi family's sheep camp.

Children always pick out a particular lamb or kid to play with when they come to visit the sheep camps. When it is time to slaughter a young sheep or goat, the older relatives make a point of informally announcing to all present the name of the animal's young owner. Not surprisingly, this often upsets children the first time it happens to them. But Paiute elders say that this is done to teach children at an early age that they must share what they have with their kin.

Today, the San Juan Paiute's main source of income is the sale of baskets. In years past, Paiute women made many types of baskets in which to cook, hold gathered foods, and carry babies. Today, there are San Juan Paiute basket weavers of all ages. Most young San Juan girls learn how to make baskets of many different patterns. Some of these are traditional, such as basketry cradle boards, and are still a part of everyday San Juan life. In the late 19th century, however, the San Juan Paiute began to produce baskets of certain color patterns solely for sale to the Navajo or to traders who would later sell them to the Navajo themselves. These items, known as "Navajo wedding baskets," are used by the Navajo in their healing ceremonies and in their traditional weddings. During a Navajo wedding, the bride and groom feed each other cornmeal moistened with water from the basket. Often, Navajo drive to Paiute camps and order their baskets in advance of a wedding. The prices range from $25 to $60 each. Although the Navajo probably used to make these baskets themselves, by the 1930s almost all Navajo wedding baskets were made either by the San Juan Paiute or by the Southern Ute in Utah and Colorado.

A Navajo wedding basket made in 1986 by San Juan Paiute Grace Lehi of Hidden Springs, Arizona. Such baskets are used as part of the traditional Navajo wedding ceremony.

More recently, the San Juan basket makers have begun to tap the more lucrative non-Indian market for their crafts. One local trader, Bill Beaver, encouraged the San Juan in this endeavor by buying baskets from them and by helping to arrange their first basketry show. In 1960, Beaver bought Sacred Mountain Trading Post, north of Flagstaff, Arizona. Beaver began to put aside some of the best baskets that the San Juan brought to him in order to create a comprehensive collection. Although he sold his first collection to the National Museum of Ethnology, in Osaka, Japan, he soon put together another. When he had amassed a large enough selection of basketry, Beaver contacted Susan Brown McGreevy and Andrew Hunter Whiteford, curators at the Wheelwright Museum of the American Indian in Santa Fe, New Mexico. In October 1985, the San Juan weavers, together with McGreevy and Whiteford, opened the San Juan Paiute's first basketry and crafts exhibition at the Wheelwright.

Since that first exhibition, the San Juan have given many more exhibitions and basketry demonstrations at museums throughout the West. They have

San Juan Paiute Bessie Owl, photographed weaving a basket in her shade house near Navajo Mountain.

also set up a basketry cooperative, using grant money from the Administration for Native Americans in Washington, D.C. Today, the San Juan weavers are able to ask much higher prices for their work than at any time in the past and give full rein to their artistic creativity. The San Juan Paiute have been able to blend their traditions with the mainstream American economy and, in doing so, have kept their uniquely Paiute way of life vital.

The San Juan, and all the other Paiute communities, have undergone many changes and survived many trials since the day when Coyote let them out of Ocean Grandmother's sack. Since the time before the arrival of Europeans, when the Paiute were self-sufficient gatherers, hunters, and farmers, these Indians have passed through times of slavery, war, devastating disease, and starvation, and finally governmental neglect. The Paiute have endured all of this and still retained much of their traditional culture. Today, the future looks brighter for the Paiute than it has for many decades. For example, the Paiute Indian Tribe of Utah has been reinstated as a tribe and the San Juan Paiute are federally recognized. The Paiute groups also have a federal agency at Cedar City that deals exclusively with Paiute issues, and all the communities are involved in projects to improve education and economic development.

At the same time, the Paiute communities have also become increasingly involved in preserving their cultural traditions. They have instituted programs to revive the use of the Paiute language and of traditional Paiute ceremonies and crafts. In this way, even as the Paiute become part of mainstream American culture, they are maintaining their distinct Paiute identity and spirit into the future. ▲

BIBLIOGRAPHY

Bunte, Pamela A., and Robert J. Franklin. *From the Sands to the Mountain: Change and Persistence in a Southern Paiute Community*. Lincoln: University of Nebraska Press, 1987.

Chavez, Fray Angelico, and Ted J. Warner, eds. *The Dominguez-Escalante Journal*. Provo, UT: Brigham Young University Press, 1976.

Euler, Robert C. *The Paiute People*. Phoenix, AZ: Indian Tribal Series, 1972.

Iverson, Peter. *The Navajos*. New York: Chelsea House, 1990.

Knack, Martha. *Life Is with People*. Socorro, NM: Ballena Press, 1980.

Sturtevant, William C., and Warren L. D'Azevedo, eds. *Handbook of North American Indians*. Vol. 11, *Great Basin*. Washington, DC: Smithsonian Institution, 1983.

Whiteford, Andrew Hunter. *Southwestern Indian Baskets*. Santa Fe, NM: School of American Research Press, 1988.

THE PAIUTE AT A GLANCE

TRIBE *Paiute or Southern Paiute*

CULTURE AREA *Great Basin*

GEOGRAPHY *Southern Great Basin and Colorado Plateau.*

LINGUISTIC FAMILY *Numic or Shoshonean branch of the Uto-Aztecan Family*

CURRENT POPULATION *Approximately 1,873*

FIRST CONTACT *Francisco Atanasio Dominguez and Silvestre Velez de Escalante, Spanish, 1776*

FEDERAL STATUS *There are five Paiute bands: the Paiute Indian tribe of Utah, the Moapa Paiute Tribe, the Kaibab Paiute Tribe, the Las Vegas Paiute Colony, and the San Juan Paiute Tribe. The Pahrump community is unrecognized and is currently seeking recognition through the Bureau of Indian Affairs' federal acknowledgment process.*

GLOSSARY

agent A person appointed by the Bureau of Indian Affairs to supervise U.S. government programs on a reservation and/or in a specific region. After 1908 the title *superintendent* replaced *agent*.

agriculture Intensive cultivation of tracts of land, sometimes using draft animals and heavy plowing equipment. Agriculture requires a largely nonnomadic life.

annuity Compensation for land and/or resources based on terms of a treaty or other agreement between the United States and an individual tribe. Annuities consisted of goods, services, and cash given to the tribe every year for a specified period.

anthropology The study of the physical, social, and historical characteristics of human beings.

archaeologist A scientist who studies past human societies through the objects, records, and settlements that people leave behind.

archaeology The recovery and reconstruction of human ways of life through the study of material culture (including tools, clothing, and food and human remains).

band A loosely organized group of people who are bound together by the need for food and defense, by family ties, and/or by other common interests.

breechcloth A strip of animal skin of cloth that is drawn between the legs and hung from a belt tied around the waist.

Bureau of Indian Affairs (BIA) A U.S. government agency now within the Department of the Interior. Originally intended to manage trade and other relations with Indians, the BIA now seeks to develop and implement programs that encourage Indians to manage their own affairs and to improve their educational opportunities and general social and economic well-being.

clan A multigenerational group having a shared identity, organization, and property based on belief in descent from a common ancestor. Because clan members consider themselves closely related, marriage within a clan is strictly prohibited.

culture The learned behavior of humans; nonbiological, socially taught activities; the way of life of a group of people.

Department of the Interior U.S. government office created in 1849 to oversee the internal affairs of the United States, including government land sales, land-related legal disputes, and American Indian affairs.

Indian Claims Commission (ICC) A U.S. government body created by an act of Congress in 1946 to hear and rule on claims brought by Indians against the United States. These claims stem from unfulfilled treaty terms, such as nonpayment for lands sold by the Indians.

Indian Reorganization Act (IRA) The 1934 federal law that ended the policy of allotting plots of land to individuals and encouraged the development of reservation communties. The act also provided for the creation of autonomous tribal governments.

mesa A high, flattopped hill; the Spanish word for table.

mission A religious center founded by advocates of a particular denomination who are trying to convert nonbelievers to their faith.

Mormon A member of the Church of Jesus Christ of Latter-day Saints.

niavi The Paiute word for chiefs.

nomadic Way of life of human societies that move frequently to follow game and other seasonal food resources and do not have one fixed place to live; the opposite of sedentary.

puagant The Paiute word for healer, meaning "one who has sacred power."

reservation, reserve A tract of land retained by Indians for their own occupation and use. Reservation is used to describe such lands in the United States; reserve, in Canada.

termination Federal policy to remove Indian tribes from government supervision and Indian lands from trust status, in effect from the late 1940s through the 1960s. The Paiute were terminated in 1957. Their tribal status was restored in 1980.

territory A defined region of the United States that is not a state but may become one. The government officials of a territory are appointed by the president, but territory residents elect their own legislature.

treaty A contract negotiated between representatives of the United States government or another national government and one or more Indian tribes. Treaties dealt with the cessation of military action, the surrender of political independence, the establishment of boundaries, terms of land sales, and related matters.

tribe A society consisting of several or many separate communities united by kinship, culture, and language, and other social institutions including clans, religious organizations, and warrior societies.

trust The relationship between the federal government and many Indian tribes, dating from the late 19th century. Government agents managed Indians' business dealings, including land transactions and rights to national resources, because the Indians were considered legally incompetent to manage their own affairs.

Yaxap A Paiute funerary ceremony, also known as the Cry, adopted from the Mojave and other tribes living to the south. During the Cry, singers chant song cycles that are meant to help guide the spirit of the deceased to his or her dwelling place in the next land.

INDEX

PICTURE CREDITS

Courtesy Pamela Bunte, pages 83, 84, 87, 88, 89, 90, 93, 94, 97, 99, 100, 101, 103; Courtesy Department of Library Services, American Museum of Natural History, photos by R. H. Lowie, pages 36 (neg. # 118694), 58 (neg. # 118676), 60 (neg. # 118646); Library of Congress, pages 20, 48; Museum of the American Indian, Heye Foundation, pages 29 (neg. # 39674), 37 (neg. # 38098), 49 (neg. # 224568), 56 (neg. # 27069), 63 (neg. # 6968), 74 (neg. # 27068), 78 (neg. # 26634); Museum of New Mexico, pages 15, 16, 17, 18; The National Archives, pages 22, 25, 28, 30, 34, 38, 50, 53, 54; New-York Historical Society, page 44; School for American Research, Santa Fe, NM, cover, pages 65–72, 102; Smithsonian Institution, National Anthropological Archives, pages 12 (neg. # 72,589-A), 19 (neg. # 85-7720), 31 (neg. # 80-19781), 33 (neg. # 85-79), 40 (neg. # 1649A); University of Nevada at Las Vegas, Special Collections, pages 42, 75, 81, 82.

Maps (pages 26, 47, 77, frontis) by Gary Tong.

ROBERT J. FRANKLIN received his B.A., M.A., and Ph.D. in anthropology from Indiana University. Dr. Franklin is the author of several articles on Southern Paiute language and culture and is coauthor with Pamela A. Bunte of *From the Sands to the Mountain,* a study of the San Juan Paiute's culture and history. Since 1982, Dr. Franklin has conducted research for the San Juan Paiute Tribe and the Native American Rights Fund on federal acknowledgment and land claim projects.

PAMELA A. BUNTE holds a B.A. from Immaculata College and an M.A. and Ph.D. in anthropology from Indiana University. She has coauthored *From the Sands to the Mountain* with Robert J. Franklin and has published a number of articles on Southern Paiute linguistics, culture, and history. Dr. Bunte has also worked with several Southern Paiute communities on development projects, including social impact assessments and Southern Paiute language renewal.

FRANK W. PORTER III, general editor of INDIANS OF NORTH AMERICA, is director of the Chelsea House Foundation for American Indian Studies. He holds a B.A., M.A., and Ph.D. from the University of Maryland. He has done extensive research concerning the Indians of Maryland and Delaware and is the author of numerous articles on their history, archaeology, geography, and ethnography. He was formerly director of the Maryland Commission on Indian Affairs and American Indian Research and Resource Institute, Gettysburg, Pennsylvania, and he has received grants from the Delaware Humanities Forum, the Maryland Committee for the Humanities, the Ford Foundation, and the National Endowment for the Humanities, among others. Dr. Porter is the author of *The Bureau of Indian Affairs* in the Chelsea House KNOW YOUR GOVERNMENT series.